Grade **1**

Scott Foresman
Weekly Tests
Teacher's Manual

Glenview, Illinois • Boston, Massachusetts • Chandler, Arizona • Upper Saddle River, New Jersey

The Pearson Promise

As the largest educational publishing company in the world, Pearson is committed to providing you with curriculum that not only meets the Common Core State Standards, but also supports your implementation of these standards with your students.

Pearson has aligned the Common Core State Standards to every grade level of *Scott Foresman Reading Street,* our premier educational curriculum. This product provides an alignment of the Common Core State Standards to the Grade 1 assessment items in *Scott Foresman Reading Street Weekly Tests.*

We value your partnership highly and look forward to continuing our mission to provide educational materials that fully satisfy your classroom needs.

ISBN-13: 978-0-328-68130-3
ISBN-10:   0-328-68130-X
4 5 6 7 8 9 10 V001 15 14 13 12

CONTENTS

Unit R My World

Unit 1 Animals, Tame and Wild

Unit 2 Communities

Unit 3 Changes

Unit 4 Treasures

Unit 5 Great Ideas

OVERVIEW

The Weekly Tests are an important part of the wide array of formal tests and classroom assessments that support instruction in Scott Foresman *Reading Street*. These tests are designed to measure children's progress based on the high-frequency words, phonics, comprehension, and writing skills taught each week. Progress on the Weekly Tests is critical for determining whether the child is mastering the weekly target skills.

This Teacher's Manual includes the following: (1) a description of the Weekly Tests, (2) instructions for administering the tests, (3) instructions for scoring and recording test results, (4) reproducible charts on which to track children's progress, (5) the answers to the tests, and (6) alignments to the Common Core State Standards (in the Item Analysis charts and at the bottom of each student test page).

DESCRIPTION OF THE WEEKLY TESTS

In Grade 1, there are 36 tests—one for each week in the Scott Foresman *Reading Street* program.

Weekly Tests R1–R6 contain 4 subtests:

- The **High-Frequency Words** subtest consists of 5 questions that assess children's knowledge of the week's high-frequency words.

- The **Word Reading** subtest consists of 5 questions that assess children's ability to decode words.

- The **Comprehension** subtest consists of a picture story and 5 questions that assess the week's target comprehension skill.

- The **Writing** subtest consists of a writing prompt that asks children to respond to the main selection in the Student Edition.

Weekly Tests 1–30 contain 4 subtests:

- The **High-Frequency Words** subtest consists of 5 multiple-choice questions that assess children's knowledge of the week's high-frequency words.

- The **Phonics** subtest consists of 5 multiple-choice questions that assess children's understanding of the week's phonics skills.

- The **Comprehension** subtest consists of a reading passage and 5 multiple-choice questions that assess the week's target comprehension skill.

- The **Writing** subtest consists of a writing prompt that asks children to respond to the main selection in the Student Edition.

ADMINISTERING THE WEEKLY TESTS

The Weekly Tests should be administered at the end of Day 5 in each week.

These tests are not intended to be timed. However, for the purposes of scheduling, planning, and practicing for timed-test situations, the Weekly Tests can be administered in 45 minutes (approximately 15 minutes for the first two subtests, 15 minutes for the Comprehension subtest, and 15 minutes for the Writing subtest).

In Unit R, **all** questions and answers must be read aloud to children (see the directions for administering Weekly Tests R1–R6 beginning on page T28). Directions in **bold** should be read aloud. Other directions are for your information. In Unit 1, you should read aloud only the questions in the High-Frequency Words and Phonics subtests. Do not read aloud the answer choices. For the Comprehension subtests, children should read the passages independently, but you should read aloud all of the questions and answer choices. You may choose whether or not to read the remaining tests aloud, based on your knowledge of your class. Be advised, however, that you should **not** read any of the **reading passages** in the Comprehension subtests aloud to children.

SCORING THE WEEKLY TESTS

Answer keys for the Weekly Tests begin on page 1. Refer to the answer key for the test you are scoring and mark each multiple-choice question as either correct (1 point) or incorrect (0 points). To score the Writing subtest, refer to the rubrics that begin on page T18.

When you have finished scoring a child's test, complete the appropriate row on the Student Progress Chart and the Class Progress Chart. Doing so allows you to keep track of children's total scores as well as their scores on each of the individual subtests. The chart can also help you monitor children's progress throughout the year.

To assess whether a child has mastered the target comprehension skill on a particular test, look at the number of items the child had correct. If the child missed more than 1 question on the target skill, then the child needs further reteaching and practice. Refer to the Item Analysis chart that begins on page T9 to identify the skills assessed on each test and the Common Core State Standard aligned to each skill.

RETEACHING OPTIONS

If a child performs poorly on a Weekly Test or shows a lack of adequate progress during the year, use the Review lessons in the Scott Foresman *Reading Street* Teacher's Editions and provide the child with additional opportunities to practice the vocabulary and target skills.

Scott Foresman *Reading Street*
Student Weekly Test Progress Chart—Grade 1

Name: _____

Test	High-Frequency Words	Word Reading/ Phonics	Comprehension	Multiple- Choice Total	Writing	TOTAL
Weekly Test R1	/5	/5	/5	/15		
Weekly Test R2	/5	/5	/5	/15		
Weekly Test R3	/5	/5	/5	/15		
Weekly Test R4	/5	/5	/5	/15		
Weekly Test R5	/5	/5	/5	/15		
Weekly Test R6	/5	/5	/5	/15		
Weekly Test 1	/5	/5	/5	/15		
Weekly Test 2	/5	/5	/5	/15		
Weekly Test 3	/5	/5	/5	/15		
Weekly Test 4	/5	/5	/5	/15		
Weekly Test 5	/5	/5	/5	/15		
Weekly Test 6	/5	/5	/5	/15		
Weekly Test 7	/5	/5	/5	/15		
Weekly Test 8	/5	/5	/5	/15		
Weekly Test 9	/5	/5	/5	/15		
Weekly Test 10	/5	/5	/5	/15		
Weekly Test 11	/5	/5	/5	/15		
Weekly Test 12	/5	/5	/5	/15		
Weekly Test 13	/5	/5	/5	/15		
Weekly Test 14	/5	/5	/5	/15		
Weekly Test 15	/5	/5	/5	/15		
Weekly Test 16	/5	/5	/5	/15		
Weekly Test 17	/5	/5	/5	/15		
Weekly Test 18	/5	/5	/5	/15		
Weekly Test 19	/5	/5	/5	/15		
Weekly Test 20	/5	/5	/5	/15		
Weekly Test 21	/5	/5	/5	/15		
Weekly Test 22	/5	/5	/5	/15		
Weekly Test 23	/5	/5	/5	/15		
Weekly Test 24	/5	/5	/5	/15		
Weekly Test 25	/5	/5	/5	/15		
Weekly Test 26	/5	/5	/5	/15		
Weekly Test 27	/5	/5	/5	/15		
Weekly Test 28	/5	/5	/5	/15		
Weekly Test 29	/5	/5	/5	/15		
Weekly Test 30	/5	/5	/5	/15		

Scott Foresman *Reading Street*
Class Weekly Test Progress Chart—Grade 1

Teacher's Name: _____

Child's Name	R1	R2	R3	R4	R5	R6	Weekly Test Total Score																												
							1	2	3	4	5	6	7	8	9	10	11	12	13	14	15	16	17	18	19	20	21	22	23	24	25	26	27	28	29	30
1																																					
2																																					
3																																					
4																																					
5																																					
6																																					
7																																					
8																																					
9																																					
10																																					
11																																					
12																																					
13																																					
14																																					
15																																					
16																																					
17																																					
18																																					
19																																					
20																																					
21																																					
22																																					
23																																					
24																																					
25																																					
26																																					
27																																					
28																																					
29																																					
30																																					

Weekly Tests Teacher's Manual

Weekly Test Item Analysis—Grade 1

TEST	SECTION	ITEMS	SKILL	COMMON CORE STATE STANDARD
Weekly Test R1	**High-Frequency Words**	1–5	Understand and use new vocabulary	Foundational Skills 3.g.
	Word Reading	6–10	Consonants *m* /m/; *s, ss* /s/; *t* /t/; Short *a*	Foundational Skills 3.b.
	Comprehension	11–15	◉ Character	Literature 7.
	Written Response	Look Back and Write	Respond to literature	Literature 7. (Also Literature 1., Language 1., 2.)
Weekly Test R2	**High-Frequency Words**	1–5	Understand and use new vocabulary	Foundational Skills 3.g.
	Word Reading	6–10	Consonants *c* /k/; *p* /p/, *n* /n/	Foundational Skills 3.b.
	Comprehension	11–15	◉ Setting	Literature 7.
	Written Response	Look Back and Write	Respond to literature	Literature 7. (Also Literature 1., 3., Language 1., 2.)
Weekly Test R3	**High-Frequency Words**	1–5	Understand and use new vocabulary	Foundational Skills 3.g.
	Word Reading	6–10	Consonants *f, ff* /f/; *b* /b/; *g* /g/; Short *i*	Foundational Skills 3.b.
	Comprehension	11–15	◉ Plot	Literature 7.
	Written Response	Look Back and Write	Respond to literature	Literature 7. (Also Literature 1., 3., Language 1., 2.)
Weekly Test R4	**High-Frequency Words**	1–5	Understand and use new vocabulary	Foundational Skills 3.g.
	Word Reading	6–10	Consonants *d* /d/; *l, ll* /l/; *h* /h/; Short *o*	Foundational Skills 3.b.
	Comprehension	11–15	◉ Realism and fantasy	Literature 7.
	Written Response	Look Back and Write	Respond to literature	Literature 7. (Also Literature 1., 3., Language 1., 2.)

Weekly Test Item Analysis—Grade 1

TEST	SECTION	ITEMS	SKILL	COMMON CORE STATE STANDARD
Weekly Test R5	**High-Frequency Words**	1–5	Understand and use new vocabulary	Foundational Skills 3.g.
	Word Reading	6–10	Consonants *r* /r/; *w* /w/; *j* /j/; *k* /k/; Short *e*	Foundational Skills 3.b.
	Comprehension	11–15	◎ Plot	Literature 3.
	Written Response	Look Back and Write	Respond to literature	Literature 7. (Also Literature 1., 3., Language 1., 2.)
Weekly Test R6	**High-Frequency Words**	1–5	Understand and use new vocabulary	Foundational Skills 3.g.
	Word Reading	6–10	Consonants *v* /v/; *y* /y/; *z, zz* /z/; *qu* /kw/ Short *u*	Foundational Skills 3.b.
	Comprehension	11–15	◎ Realism and fantasy	Literature 5.
	Written Response	Look Back and Write	Respond to literature	Literature 7. (Also Literature 1., 3., Language 1., 2.)
Weekly Test 1	**High-Frequency Words**	1–5	Understand and use new vocabulary	Foundational Skills 3.g.
	Phonics	6–10	Short *a*, Consonant pattern -*ck*	Foundational Skills 3.b.
	Comprehension	11–15	◎ Character and setting	Literature 3.
	Written Response	Look Back and Write	Respond to literature	Literature 7. (Also Literature 1., 3., Language 1., 2.)
Weekly Test 2	**High-Frequency Words**	1–5	Understand and use new vocabulary	Foundational Skills 3.g.
	Phonics	6–10	Short *i;* Consonant *x* /ks/	Foundational Skills 3.b.
	Comprehension	11–15	◎ Plot	Literature 3.
	Written Response	Look Back and Write	Respond to literature	Literature 7. (Also Literature 1., 3., Language 1., 2.)

Weekly Test Item Analysis—Grade 1

TEST	SECTION	ITEMS	SKILL	COMMON CORE STATE STANDARD
Weekly Test 3	**High-Frequency Words**	1–5	Understand and use new vocabulary	Foundational Skills 3.g.
	Phonics	6–10	Short *o;* Plural *-s;* Consonant *s/z/*	Foundational Skills 3.b.
	Comprehension	11–15	◎ Character	Literature 3.
	Written Response	Look Back and Write	Respond to literature	Literature 7. (Also Literature 1., 3., Language 1., 2.)
Weekly Test 4	**High-Frequency Words**	1–5	Understand and use new vocabulary	Foundational Skills 3.g.
	Phonics	6–10	Inflected ending *-s;* Inflected ending *-ing*	Foundational Skills 3.f.
	Comprehension	11–15	◎ Main idea and details	Informational Text 2.
	Written Response	Look Back and Write	Respond to literature	Informational Text 3. (Also Informational Text 2., 7., Writing 2., Language 1., 2.)
Weekly Test 5	**High-Frequency Words**	1–5	Understand and use new vocabulary	Foundational Skills 3.g.
	Phonics	6–10	Short *e;* Initial consonant blends	Foundational Skills 3.b.
	Comprehension	11–15	◎ Main idea and details	Literature 2.
	Written Response	Look Back and Write	Respond to literature	Literature 3. (Also Literature 1., 7., Language 1., 2.)
Weekly Test 6	**High-Frequency Words**	1–5	Understand and use new vocabulary	Foundational Skills 3.g.
	Phonics	6–10	Short *u;* Final Consonant blends	Foundational Skills 3.b.
	Comprehension	11–15	◎ Cause and effect	Literature 1.
	Written Response	Look Back and Write	Respond to literature	Writing 2. (Also Informational Text 6., Informational Text 7., Language 1., 2.)

Weekly Test Item Analysis—Grade 1

TEST	SECTION	ITEMS	SKILL	COMMON CORE STATE STANDARD
Weekly Test 7	**High-Frequency Words**	1–5	Understand and use new vocabulary	Foundational Skills 3.g.
	Phonics	6–10	Consonant digraphs *sh, th;* Vowel sound in *ball: a, al*	6–8: Foundational Skills 3.a. 9–10: Foundational Skills 3.
	Comprehension	11–15	◉ Sequence	Literature 3.
	Written Response	Look Back and Write	Respond to literature	Writing 2. (Also Language 1., 2.)
Weekly Test 8	**High-Frequency Words**	1–5	Understand and use new vocabulary	Foundational Skills 3.g.
	Phonics	6–10	Long *a;* Consonants *c* /s/; *g* /j/	6–9: Foundational Skills 3.c. 10: Foundational Skills 3.
	Comprehension	11–15	◉ Cause and effect	Literature 1.
	Written Response	Look Back and Write	Respond to literature	Writing 2. (Also Language 1., 2.)
Weekly Test 9	**High-Frequency Words**	1–5	Understand and use new vocabulary	Foundational Skills 3.g.
	Phonics	6–10	Long *i;* Consonant digraphs *wh, ch, tch, ph*	6–7: Foundational Skills 3.c. 8–10: Foundational Skills 3.
	Comprehension	11–15	◉ Author's purpose	11–14: Literature 3. 15: Literature 1.
	Written Response	Look Back and Write	Respond to literature	Writing 2. (Also Language 1., 2.)
Weekly Test 10	**High-Frequency Words**	1–5	Understand and use new vocabulary	Foundational Skills 3.g.
	Phonics	6–10	Long *o;* Contractions	6–7: Foundational Skills 3.c. 8–10: Foundational Skills 3.
	Comprehension	11–15	◉ Sequence	Literature 3.
	Written Response	Look Back and Write	Respond to literature	Writing 2. (Also Language 1., 2.)

Weekly Test Item Analysis—Grade 1

TEST	SECTION	ITEMS	SKILL	COMMON CORE STATE STANDARD
Weekly Test 11	**High-Frequency Words**	1–5	Understand and use new vocabulary	Foundational Skills 3.g.
	Phonics	6–10	Long *u*, long *e;* Inflected ending *-ed*	6–7: Foundational Skills 3.c. 8–10: Foundational Skills 3.f.
	Comprehension	11–15	◎ Author's purpose	11–14: Informational Text 2. 15: Informational Text 8.
	Written Response	Look Back and Write	Respond to literature	Writing 2. (Also Language 1., 2.)
Weekly Test 12	**High-Frequency Words**	1–5	Understand and use new vocabulary	Foundational Skills 3.g.
	Phonics	6–10	Long *e;* Syllables VC/CV	6–7: Foundational Skills 3.c. 8–10: Foundational Skills 3.d.
	Comprehension	11–15	◎ Compare and contrast	11: Informational Text 8. 12–15: Informational Text 3.
	Written Response	Look Back and Write	Respond to literature	Writing 2. (Also Language 1., 2.)
Weekly Test 13	**High-Frequency Words**	1–5	Understand and use new vocabulary	Foundational Skills 3.g.
	Phonics	6–10	Vowel sound of *y;* Syllable pattern CV	Foundational Skills 3.
	Comprehension	11–15	◎ Sequence	Informational Text 1.
	Written Response	Look Back and Write	Respond to literature	Writing 2. (Also Language 1., 2.)
Weekly Test 14	**High-Frequency Words**	1–5	Understand and use new vocabulary	Foundational Skills 3.g.
	Phonics	6–10	Consonant patterns *ng, nk;* Compound words	Foundational Skills 3.
	Comprehension	11–15	◎ Compare and contrast	Literature 9.
	Written Response	Look Back and Write	Respond to literature	Writing 3. (Also Literature 7., Language 1., 2.)

Weekly Test Item Analysis—Grade 1

TEST	SECTION	ITEMS	SKILL	COMMON CORE STATE STANDARD
Weekly Test 15	**High-Frequency Words**	1–5	Understand and use new vocabulary	Foundational Skills 3.g.
	Phonics	6–10	Ending *es;* Vowel: *r*-controlled *or, ore*	6–7: Foundational Skills 3. 8–10: Foundational Skills 3.f.
	Comprehension	11–15	◎ Fact and opinion	Informational Text 1.
	Written Response	Look Back and Write	Respond to literature	Writing 2. (Also Language 1., 2.)
Weekly Test 16	**High-Frequency Words**	1–5	Understand and use new vocabulary	Foundational Skills 3.g.
	Phonics	6–10	Adding endings: Vowel: *r*-controlled *ar*	6–7: Foundational Skills 3. 8–10: Foundational Skills 3.f.
	Comprehension	11–15	◎ Author's purpose	Informational Text 8.
	Written Response	Look Back and Write	Respond to literature	Writing 2. (Also Language 1., 2.)
Weekly Test 17	**High-Frequency Words**	1–5	Understand and use new vocabulary	Foundational Skills 3.g.
	Phonics	6–10	Vowel: *r*-controlled *er, ir, ur;* Contractions	Foundational Skills 3.
	Comprehension	11–15	◎ Fact and opinion	Informational Text 1.
	Written Response	Look Back and Write	Respond to literature	Writing 2. (Also Informational Text 3., Writing 5., Language 1., 2.)
Weekly Test 18	**High-Frequency Words**	1–5	Understand and use new vocabulary	Foundational Skills 3.g.
	Phonics	6–10	Comparative endings *-er, -est;* Consonant pattern *-dge*	Foundational Skills 3.
	Comprehension	11–15	◎ Draw conclusions	Literature 1.
	Written Response	Look Back and Write	Respond to literature	Writing 2. (Also Language 1., 2.)

Weekly Test Item Analysis—Grade 1

TEST	SECTION	ITEMS	SKILL	COMMON CORE STATE STANDARD
Weekly Test 19	**High-Frequency Words**	1–5	Understand and use new vocabulary	Foundational Skills 3.g.
	Phonics	6–10	Vowel digraphs *ai, ay;* Singular and plural possessives	6–8: Foundational Skills 3.c. 9–10: Foundational Skills 3.
	Comprehension	11–15	◉ Draw conclusions	Literature 1.
	Written Response	Look Back and Write	Respond to literature	Literature 3. (Also Literature 1., 7., Language 1., 2.)
Weekly Test 20	**High-Frequency Words**	1–5	Understand and use new vocabulary	Foundational Skills 3.g.
	Phonics	6–10	Vowel digraphs *ea;* Adding endings	6–7: Foundational Skills 3.c. 8–10: Foundational Skills 3.f.
	Comprehension	11–15	◉ Theme	Literature 2.
	Written Response	Look Back and Write	Respond to literature	Literature 3. (Also Literature 1., 4., 7., Language 1., 2.)
Weekly Test 21	**High-Frequency Words**	1–5	Understand and use new vocabulary	Foundational Skills 3.g.
	Phonics	6–10	Vowel digraphs *oa, ow;* Three-letter consonant blends	6–8: Foundational Skills 3.c. 9–10: Foundational Skills 3.
	Comprehension	11–15	◉ Facts and details	Informational Text 2.
	Written Response	Look Back and Write	Respond to literature	Writing 2. (Also Informational Text 7., Language 1., 2.)
Weekly Test 22	**High-Frequency Words**	1–5	Understand and use new vocabulary	Foundational Skills 3.g.
	Phonics	6–10	Vowel digraphs *ie, igh;* Consonant patterns *kn, wr*	6–8: Foundational Skills 3.c. 9–10: Foundational Skills 3.
	Comprehension	11–15	◉ Facts and details	Informational Text 1.
	Written Response	Look Back and Write	Respond to literature	Writing 2. (Also Informational Text 7., Language 1., 2.)

Weekly Test Item Analysis—Grade 1

TEST	SECTION	ITEMS	SKILL	COMMON CORE STATE STANDARD
Weekly Test 23	**High-Frequency Words**	1–5	Understand and use new vocabulary	Foundational Skills 3.g.
	Phonics	6–10	Compound words; Vowel digraphs *ue, ew, ui*	6–8: Foundational Skills 3. 9–10: Foundational Skills 3.e.
	Comprehension	11–15	◉ Theme	11: Literature 2. 12–15: Literature 3.
	Written Response	Look Back and Write	Respond to literature	Literature 3. (Also Literature 1., 7., Language 1., 2.)
Weekly Test 24	**High-Frequency Words**	1–5	Understand and use new vocabulary	Foundational Skills 3.g.
	Phonics	6–10	Vowel sound in *moon: oo;* Suffixes *-ly, -ful*	Foundational Skills 3.
	Comprehension	11–15	◉ Cause and effect	Literature 3.
	Written Response	Look Back and Write	Respond to literature	Literature 3. (Also Literature 1., 7., Language 1., 2.)
Weekly Test 25	**High-Frequency Words**	1–5	Understand and use new vocabulary	Foundational Skills 3.g.
	Phonics	6–10	Diphthongs *ow, ou;* Final syllable *-le*	6–7: Foundational Skills 3. 8–10: Foundational Skills 3.e.
	Comprehension	11–15	◉ Character, setting and plot	Literature 3.
	Written Response	Look Back and Write	Respond to literature	Literature 3. (Also Literature 1., 7., Language 1., 2.)
Weekly Test 26	**High-Frequency Words**	1–5	Understand and use new vocabulary	Foundational Skills 3.g.
	Phonics	6–10	Vowel patterns *ow, ou;* Syllables V/CV, VC/V	6–7: Foundational Skills 3. 8–10: Foundational Skills 3.e.
	Comprehension	11–15	◉ Draw conclusions	Literature 3.
	Written Response	Look Back and Write	Respond to literature	Literature 3. (Also Literature 1., 7., Language 1., 2.)

Weekly Test Item Analysis—Grade 1

TEST	SECTION	ITEMS	SKILL	COMMON CORE STATE STANDARD
Weekly Test 27	**High-Frequency Words**	1–5	Understand and use new vocabulary	Foundational Skills 3.g.
	Phonics	6–10	Vowel sound in *foot: oo;* Adding endings	6–7: Foundational Skills 3. 8–10: Foundational Skills 3.f.
	Comprehension	11–15	◎ Compare and contrast	Informational Text 3.
	Written Response	Look Back and Write	Respond to literature	Informational Text 7. (Also Informational Text 1., Writing 2., Language 1., 2.)
Weekly Test 28	**High-Frequency Words**	1–5	Understand and use new vocabulary	Foundational Skills 3.g.
	Phonics	6–10	Diphthongs *oi, oy;* Suffixes *-er, -or*	Foundational Skills 3.
	Comprehension	11–15	◎ Main idea and details	Informational Text 2.
	Written Response	Look Back and Write	Respond to literature	Informational Text 7. (Also Information Text 1., Language 1., 2.)
Weekly Test 29	**High-Frequency Words**	1–5	Understand and use new vocabulary	Foundational Skills 3.g.
	Phonics	6–10	Vowel sound in *ball: aw, au;* Syllable patterns: Vowel digraphs and diphthongs	6–7: Foundational Skills 3.e. 8–10: Foundational Skills 3.
	Comprehension	11–15	◎ Sequence	Informational Text 1.
	Written Response	Look Back and Write	Respond to literature	Writing 2. (Also Informational Text 1., Language 1., 2.)
Weekly Test 30	**High-Frequency Words**	1–5	Understand and use new vocabulary	Foundational Skills 3.g.
	Phonics	6–10	Prefixes *un- re-;* Long *o,* long *i*	Foundational Skills 3.
	Comprehension	11–15	◎ Theme	Literature 2.
	Written Response	Look Back and Write	Respond to literature	Writing 2. (Also Literature 1., 2., 3., Language 1., 2.)

COMPREHENSION TARGET SKILL COVERAGE

How can the Weekly Tests predict student success on Unit Benchmark Tests?

Each Unit Benchmark Test, as well as assessing overall student reading ability, concentrates on two skills taught and/or reviewed during the unit by including several questions on those skills. In order to ensure that comprehension target skill can be accurately learned and then tested, students learn each target skill through a combination of being taught and reviewing the skill multiple times before testing occurs. The charts below show the units/weeks where the target comprehension skills are taught and where they are tested on Weekly Tests. Based on the student's number of correct answers for each tested target skill, the teacher will know whether a student has gained the necessary skill knowledge before the Unit Test is given. A low score on the Weekly Tests probably indicates a need for closer review of the student's performance and perhaps additional instruction. It is important to understand that these tests provide only one look at the student's progress and should be interpreted in conjunction with other assessments and the teacher's observation.

Using the Comprehension Target Skill Coverage Chart

To score target skill knowledge, use the Comprehension Target Skill Coverage Chart.

1. Make a copy of the appropriate Comprehension Target Skill Coverage chart for each student.

2. To score, circle the number of correct answers the student had for that skill on the appropriate Weekly Test.

3. Using the total number of correct answers for a skill, check the appropriate box under *Student Trend* to indicate whether or not the student has acquired the target skill knowledge. We recommend 90% correct as the criterion for skill aquisition at this level. Add any notes or observations that may be helpful to you and the student in later instruction.

GRADE 1 — COMPREHENSION TARGET SKILL COVERAGE CHART

Student Name _____

Unit R Tested Skills	Weekly Test Locations	Number Correct	Student Trend
Literary Element: Plot **Common Core State Standards** Literature 3., Literature 7.	Weekly Test R3	0 1 2 3 4 5	_____ Skill knowledge acquired
	Weekly Test R5	0 1 2 3 4 5	_____ Skill needs further review
Realism and Fantasy **Common Core State Standards** Literature 5., Literature 7.	Weekly Test R4	0 1 2 3 4 5	_____ Skill knowledge acquired
	Weekly Test R6	0 1 2 3 4 5	_____ Skill needs further review

Unit 1 Tested Skills	Weekly Test Locations	Number Correct	Student Trend
Literary Elements: Character/Setting **Common Core State Standards** Literature 3., Literature 7.	Weekly Test R1	0 1 2 3 4 5	
	Weekly Test R2	0 1 2 3 4 5	_____ Skill knowledge acquired
	Weekly Test 1	0 1 2 3 4 5	_____ Skill needs further review
	Weekly Test 3	0 1 2 3 4 5	
Main Idea and Details **Common Core State Standards** Literature 2.; Informational Text 2.	Weekly Test 4	0 1 2 3 4 5	_____ Skill knowledge acquired
	Weekly Test 5	0 1 2 3 4 5	_____ Skill needs further review

GRADE 1 — COMPREHENSION TARGET SKILL COVERAGE CHART

Student Name _____

Unit 2 Tested Skills	Weekly Test Locations	Number Correct	Student Trend
Cause and Effect **Common Core State Standards** Literature 1., Literature 3.	Weekly Test 6	0 1 2 3 4 5	_____ Skill knowledge acquired
	Weekly Test 8	0 1 2 3 4 5	_____ Skill needs further review
Author's Purpose **Common Core State Standards** Literature 1.; Informational Text 8.	Weekly Test 9	0 1 2 3 4 5	_____ Skill knowledge acquired
	Weekly Test 11	0 1 2 3 4 5	_____ Skill needs further review

Unit 3 Tested Skills	Weekly Test Locations	Number Correct	Student Trend
Sequence **Common Core State Standards** Literature 3.; Informational Text 1.	Weekly Test 7	0 1 2 3 4 5	_____ Skill knowledge acquired
	Weekly Test 10	0 1 2 3 4 5	
	Weekly Test 13	0 1 2 3 4 5	_____ Skill needs further review
Compare and Contrast **Common Core State Standards** Literature 9.; Informational Text 3.	Weekly Test 12	0 1 2 3 4 5	_____ Skill knowledge acquired
	Weekly Test 14	0 1 2 3 4 5	_____ Skill needs further review

GRADE 1 — COMPREHENSION TARGET SKILL COVERAGE CHART

Student Name _____

Unit 4 Tested Skills	Weekly Test Locations	Number Correct	Student Trend
Fact and Opinion **Common Core State Standards** Informational Text 1.	Weekly Test 15	0 1 2 3 4 5	_____ Skill knowledge acquired
	Weekly Test 17	0 1 2 3 4 5	_____ Skill needs further review
Draw Conclusions **Common Core State Standards** Literature 1., Literature 3.	Weekly Test 18	0 1 2 3 4 5	_____ Skill knowledge acquired
	Weekly Test 19	0 1 2 3 4 5	_____ Skill needs further review

Unit 5 Tested Skills	Weekly Test Locations	Number Correct	Student Trend
Literary Element: Theme **Common Core State Standards** Literature 2.	Weekly Test 20	0 1 2 3 4 5	_____ Skill knowledge acquired
	Weekly Test 23	0 1 2 3 4 5	
	Weekly Test 30	0 1 2 3 4 5	_____ Skill needs further review
Facts and Details **Common Core State Standards** Informational Text 1., Informational Text 2.	Weekly Test 21	0 1 2 3 4 5	_____ Skill knowledge acquired
	Weekly Test 22	0 1 2 3 4 5	_____ Skill needs further review

SCORING RUBRICS FOR WRITING

Use one of the following rubrics (2 points or 4 points depending on your needs) to evaluate responses on the Writing subtest. Suggested top-score responses for each week's prompt follow the rubrics.

Two-Point Scoring Rubric

2 points:

The response indicates that the child has a complete understanding of the reading concept embodied in the task. The response is accurate and complete, and fulfills all the requirements of the task. Necessary support and/or examples are included, and the information given is clearly text-based.

1 point:

The response indicates that the child has a partial understanding of the reading concept embodied in the task. The response includes information that is essentially correct and text-based, but the information is too general or too simplistic. Some of the support and/or examples may be incomplete or omitted.

0 points:

The response indicates that the child does not demonstrate an understanding of the reading concept embodied in the task. The child has either failed to respond or has provided a response that is inaccurate or has insufficient information.

Four-Point Scoring Rubric

4 points:

The response indicates that the child has a thorough understanding of the reading concept embodied in the task. The response is accurate and complete, and fulfills all the requirements of the task. Necessary support and/or examples are included, and the information given is clearly text-based.

3 points:

The response indicates that the child has an understanding of the reading concept embodied in the task. The response is accurate and fulfills all the requirements of the task, but the required support and/or details are not complete or clearly text-based.

2 points:

The response indicates that the child has a partial understanding of the reading concept embodied in the task. The response includes information that is essentially correct and text-based, but the information is too general or too simplistic. Some of the support and/or examples and requirements of the task may be incomplete or omitted.

1 point:

The response indicates that the child has a very limited understanding of the reading concept embodied in the task. The response is incomplete, may exhibit many flaws, and may not address all the requirements of the task.

0 points:

The response indicates that the child does not demonstrate an understanding of the reading concept embodied in the task. The child has either failed to respond or has provided a response that is inaccurate or has insufficient information.

Top-Level Responses

Weekly Test R1:

Top-Score Response A top-score response uses details from the text and the pictures to tell where Tam is and the things that are there. For example:

Tam is in Sam's room. I see a bed. I see a book.

Weekly Test R2:

Top-Score Response A top-score response uses details from the text and the pictures to tell about who comes to Sam's house and what he does. For example:

Mac comes to Sam's house. Mac snaps a picture. Sam's family will like the picture.

Weekly Test R3:

Top-Score Response A top-score response uses what children know, details from the text, and the picture to tell about where Tip and Tam are on page 83. For example:

Tip and Tam are both in the bag. I see them in the picture. I read the part that tells about where Tip and Tam are.

Weekly Test R4:

Top-Score Response A top-score response uses details from the text and the pictures to tell what Pam and Dot like to do. For example:

Pam and Dot like to hop. They hop fast. Pam and Dot sit on a mat.

Weekly Test R5:

Top-Score Response A top-score response uses details from the text and the pictures to tell what Kim, Jill, and Pat will do. For example:

Pat will show his jet. Jill will jig. Kim will show her mat.

Weekly Test R6:

Top-Score Response A top-score response uses information from the text and the pictures to describe a variety of materials sold at the farmers market. For example:

You can buy fruits and vegetables at a farmers market. One kind of fruit you can buy is an apple. Another kind is a banana.

Weekly Test 1:

Top-Score Response A top-score response uses details from the text and the pictures to explain where Sam ran. For example:

Sam ran to the sack. He hid there. I think he hid there so that the dog would not find him.

Weekly Test 2:

Top-Score Response A top-score response uses details from the text and the pictures to tell how Pig feels at the end of the story. For example:

Pig feels happy. She does a jig. She felt better after she took medicine.

Weekly Test 3:

Top-Score Response A top-score response uses details from the text and the pictures to tell how Ox can help. For example:

Ox can mop the pigs and fix the wigs. Ox can help Mom and Pop go to town. Ox can pack a sack and take it back. Ox can use big pans and big fans.

Weekly Test 4:

Top-Score Response A top-score response uses details from the text and the picture to tell how the fox takes care of her kit. For example:

The fox takes care of her kit by picking him up and moving him if he is on the rocks.

Weekly Test 5:

Top-Score Response A top-score response uses details from the text and the pictures to tell how Brad and Kim saved the egg. For example:

Brad and Kim used the net to get the egg. Then they put the egg back in the nest.

Weekly Test 6:

Top-Score Response A top-score response uses details from the text and the pictures to tell about an animal pictured in the selection. For example:

Some big hippos are sitting in mud. It is hot out. The wet mud keeps the hippos cool.

Weekly Test 7:

Top-Score Response A top-score response uses details from pages 30–31 to tell where Max gets a big fish. For example:

First, Grandma and Ruby and Max walk to a fish shop. The fish man has lots of fish in a box. Grandma picks a good fish and gets it for Max.

Weekly Test 8:

Top-Score Response A top-score response uses details from the text and the pictures to tell about an actor in the play. For example:

Dave wants to be a pig in the play. He makes an odd pig mask with a hat and tie.

Weekly Test 9:

Top-Score Response A top-score response uses details from the text and the pictures to tell what job a worker does. For example:

Firefighters help to stop fires. They keep us safe from fires.

Weekly Test 10:

Top-Score Response A top-score response uses details from the text and the pictures to tell how the community helped each other. For example:

The triceratops stayed in the circle. They drove back T. Rex. The community worked together to keep the baby safe.

Weekly Test 11:

Top-Score Response A top-score response uses details from the text and photos throughout the selection to tell about one animal that lives in a forest. For example:

Bears live in the forest. They can climb the trees.

Weekly Test 12:

Top-Score Response A top-score response uses details from the text and the pictures on page 183 to tell about the queen bee's job. For example:

The queen bee rules the hive. She is helped by the worker bees.

Weekly Test 13:

Top-Score Response A top-score response uses details from the text and the picture to tell why a sunny spot is good for growing plants. For example:

Mom and Dad plant in the sunny spot to help the plants grow. The plants also make the building look nice.

Weekly Test 14:

Top-Score Response A top-score response uses details from the text and the pictures to tell how Ruby changed as she got bigger. For example:

Ruby's feathers got fluffy. Her wings became wide and beautiful.

Weekly Test 15:

Top-Score Response A top-score response uses details from the text and the pictures to explain why the mother keeps her babies in the nest. For example:

The mother mouse keeps the babies safe in the nest. They have no fur and can't see. They are weak. If they left the nest, they could get hurt.

Weekly Test 16:

Top-Score Response A top-score response gives specific details from the text to tell what advice Frog gave Toad. For example:

Frog told Toad to leave the seeds alone for a few days. He said to let the sun and rain help the seeds grow.

Weekly Test 17:

Top-Score Response A top-score response uses facts from the text and inference to tell why these butterflies aren't afraid of birds. For example:

These butterflies aren't afraid of birds because birds will not eat these butterflies. The birds know that these butterflies taste awful.

Weekly Test 18:

Top-Score Response A top-score response uses details from the text and the pictures to tell where animals go when the days turn cold. For example:

When the days turn cold, geese and hummingbirds fly to a warmer place.

Weekly Test 19:

Top-Score Response A top-score response uses details from the text and the pictures to tell what Francisco gives Mama for a birthday present. For example:

Francisco gives his Mama a surprise party for her present. He plans the party. He helps get everything ready. Mama is so happy to have all her family and friends with her.

Weekly Test 20:

Top-Score Response A top-score response uses details from the text and the pictures to explain why Cinderella is sad. For example:

Cinderella is sad because she wants to go to the ball. Her sisters get new dresses and she doesn't. Her sisters go to the ball and she can't. She has to clean the house while her sisters have fun.

Weekly Test 21:

Top-Score Response A top-score response uses details from the text and the pictures to tell about one thing that can be seen in Washington, D.C. For example:

One thing you can see in Washington, D.C., is the White House. It is where the President lives and works.

Weekly Test 22:

Top-Score Response A top-score response uses facts and details from the text and the pictures to tell how ranch hands keep the herd together. For example:

Ranch hands ride well-trained horses. The horses help keep the cows together. If cows run off, the ranch hand must chase them and bring them back.

Weekly Test 23:

Top-Score Response A top-score response uses details from the story to tell why Peter takes his chair to his room. For example:

It is Peter's special chair from when he was little. He is afraid his parents will paint it pink.

Weekly Test 24:

Top-Score Response A top-score response uses details from the text and the pictures to tell which costumes Henry and Mudge tried on. For example:

Mudge tried on a wig and a bow. The wig made him look like a poodle. Henry tried on a tuxedo, a hat, and some shiny shoes.

Weekly Test 25:

Top-Score Response A top-score response uses details from the story to tell why Little Chick's idea was a great solution to her problem. For example:

Little Chick ran tippy-toe around the tree as Dog chased her. Dog's rope wrapped around the tree. Dog could not reach Little Chick. Hen and her chicks could get into the garden now.

Weekly Test 26:

Top-Score Response A top-score response uses details from the text and the pictures to tell why Mole thought he was flying. For example:

The wind was strong on the hill. Mole was way up high. He saw the sky and the birds. The wind moved him around. He thought his feet were not on the ground.

Weekly Test 27:

Top-Score Response A top-score response uses details from the selection to tell how maple seeds travel. For example:

Maple seeds have wings. The wings twirl and the seeds ride the wind.

Weekly Test 28:

Top-Score Response A top-score response uses details from the text and the pictures to tell how to use an inclined plane to get a box into a truck. For example:

First put an inclined plane at the back of a truck. Then put the big box on a dolly with wheels. Last, push the box up the ramp to get it on the truck.

Weekly Test 29:

Top-Score Response A top-score response uses details from the selection to tell what Aleck Bell was like when he was a boy. For example:

Aleck Bell liked playing the piano. He taught others to play, too.

He liked watching his dad teach deaf children to speak. Aleck wanted to teach deaf people like his dad.

Aleck liked inventing things. He invented a tool. He also invented something to make it look like his dog could talk!

Weekly Test 30:

Top-Score Response A top-score response uses details from the text and the pictures to tell what grew in Momoko's garden. For example:

Rose bushes grew in the old tires in Momoko's garden. Tomatoes, carrots, and peas grew in the crates. Apple trees, a butterfly bush, and some herbs also grew in the garden.

Directions
Weekly Test R1

HIGH-FREQUENCY WORDS

Turn to page 1. Use the following directions to administer the assessment. Children are to respond by circling the answer to each question. If children are unfamiliar with circling answers, draw three pictures in a row on the chalkboard and demonstrate how to draw a circle around one of the pictures.

As you say a word aloud, the child will circle it. Move through the assessment quickly to make sure you are assessing the child's ability to recognize the high-frequency words quickly.

Turn to page 1 in your booklet. I am going to say a word in each row, and you are going to circle the word I am saying.

1. **Find the row marked number 1. Look at the three words. Circle the word** *green...green.*

2. **Find the row marked number 2. Look at the three words. Circle the word** *see...see.*

3. **Find the row marked number 3. Look at the three words. Circle the word** *a...a.*

4. **Find the row marked number 4. Look at the three words. Circle the word** *I...I.*

5. **Find the row marked number 5. Look at the three words. Circle the word** *green...green.*

WORD READING

Turn to page 2. As you say a word aloud, the child will circle it. Move through this assessment a bit more slowly than you did for high-frequency words. You are assessing the child's ability to decode, and the child needs a little bit of time to do this.

Turn to page 2 in your booklet. For the next part, I am going to do the same thing. I am going to say a word in each row, and you are going to circle the word I am saying.

6. **Find the row marked number 6. Look at the three words. Circle the word** *at...at.*

7. **Find the row marked number 7. Look at the three words. Circle the name** *Tam...Tam.*

8. **Find the row marked number 8. Look at the three words. Circle the word** *sat...sat.*

9. **Find the row marked number 9. Look at the three words. Circle the name** *Sam...Sam.*

10. **Find the row marked number 10. Look at the three words. Circle the word** *mat...mat.*

COMPREHENSION

Turn to page 3 and have children look at the pictures. Read the questions and all of the answer choices on page 4 aloud to the class.

Instead of circling the answer, you are going to fill in the small circle beside the correct answer.

If children are unfamiliar with filling in circles, draw one on the chalkboard and demonstrate filling it in.

WRITING

Turn to page 5. Read the prompt and tips aloud to children.

Now you are going to write an answer to a question about the story you read in your student book this week. Write your answer on the lines on page 6.

Weekly Test R2

HIGH-FREQUENCY WORDS

Turn to page 7. Use the following directions to administer the test. As you say a word aloud, the child will circle it. Move through the assessment quickly to make sure you are assessing the child's ability to recognize the high-frequency words quickly.

Turn to page 7 in your booklet. Now I am going to say a word in each row, and you are going to circle the word I am saying.

1. **Find the row marked number 1. Look at the three words. Circle the word** *like…like*.

2. **Find the row marked number 2. Look at the three words. Circle the word** *we…we*.

3. **Find the row marked number 3. Look at the three words. Circle the word** *the…the*.

4. **Find the row marked number 4. Look at the three words. Circle the word** *one…one*.

5. **Find the row marked number 5. Look at the three words. Circle the word** *like…like*.

WORD READING

Turn to page 8. As you say a word aloud, the child will circle it. Move through this assessment a bit more slowly than you did for high-frequency words. You are assessing the child's ability to decode, and the child needs a little bit of time to do this.

Turn to page 8 in your booklet. Now you are going to circle the word in each row that is shown in the picture.

6. **Find the row marked number 6. Look at the picture. It is a** *cat*. **Look at the three words in the same row. Circle the word** *cat…cat*.

7. **Find the row marked number 7. Look at the picture. It is a** *pan*. **Look at the three words in the same row. Circle the word** *pan…pan*.

8. **Find the row marked number 8. Look at the picture. It is a** *map*. **Look at the three words in the same row. Circle the word** *map…map*.

9. **Find the row marked number 9. Look at the picture. It is a** *can*. **Look at the three words in the same row. Circle the word** *can…can*.

10. **Find the row marked number 10. Look at the picture. It is a** *cap*. **Look at the three words in the same row. Circle the word** *cap…cap*.

Weekly Tests Teacher's Manual

COMPREHENSION

Turn to page 9 and have children look at the picture. Read the questions and all of the answer choices on page 10 aloud to the class.

WRITING

Turn to page 11. Read the prompt and tips aloud to children.

Weekly Test R3

HIGH-FREQUENCY WORDS

Turn to page 13. Use the following directions to administer the assessment.

As you say a word aloud, the child will circle it. Move through the assessment quickly to make sure you are assessing the child's ability to recognize the high-frequency words quickly.

Turn to page 13 in your booklet. I am going to say a word in each row, and you are going to circle the word I am saying.

1. **Find the row marked number 1. Look at the three words. Circle the word** *do…do*.

2. **Find the row marked number 2. Look at the three words. Circle the word** *look…look*.

3. **Find the row marked number 3. Look at the three words. Circle the word** *you…you*.

4. **Find the row marked number 4. Look at the three words. Circle the word** *was…was*.

5. **Find the row marked number 5. Look at the three words. Circle the word** *yellow…yellow*.

WORD READING

Turn to page 14. As you say a word aloud, the child will circle it. Move through this assessment a bit more slowly than you did for high-frequency words. You are assessing the child's ability to decode, and the child needs a little bit of time to do this.

Turn to page 14 in your booklet. Now you are going to circle the word in each row that is shown in the picture.

6. **Find the row marked number 6. Look at the picture. It is a** *pin*. **Look at the three words in the same row. Circle the word** *pin…pin*.

7. **Find the row marked number 7. Look at the picture. It is a** *bag*. **Look at the three words in the same row. Circle the word** *bag…bag*.

8. **Find the row marked number 8. Look at the picture. It is a** *pig*. **Look at the three words in the same row. Circle the word** *pig…pig*.

9. **Find the row marked number 9. Look at the picture. It is a** *cab*. **Look at the three words in the same row. Circle the word** *cab…cab*.

10. **Find the row marked number 10. Look at the picture. It is a** *fan*. **Look at the three words in the same row. Circle the word** *fan…fan*.

COMPREHENSION

Turn to page 15 and have children look at the pictures. Read the questions and all of the answer choices aloud to the class.

WRITING

Turn to page 17. Read the prompt and tips aloud to children.

Weekly Test R4

HIGH-FREQUENCY WORDS

Turn to page 19. Use the following directions to administer the assessment.

As you say a word aloud, the child will circle it. Move through the assessment quickly to make sure you are assessing the child's ability to recognize the high-frequency words quickly.

Turn to page 19 in your booklet. I am going to say a word in each row, and you are going to circle the word I am saying.

1. **Find the row marked number 1. Look at the three words. Circle the word** *are…are.*

2. **Find the row marked number 2. Look at the three words. Circle the word** *have…have.*

3. **Find the row marked number 3. Look at the three words. Circle the word** *they…they.*

4. **Find the row marked number 4. Look at the three words. Circle the word** *that…that.*

5. **Find the row marked number 5. Look at the three words. Circle the word** *two…two.*

WORD READING

Turn to page 20. Children are to circle the word shown in the picture. Move through this assessment a bit more slowly than you did for high-frequency words. You are assessing the child's ability to decode, and the child needs a little bit of time to do this.

Turn to page 20 in your booklet. Now you are going to circle the word in each row that is shown in the picture.

6. **Find the row marked number 6. Look at the picture. It is a** *mop.* **Look at the three words in the same row. Circle the word** *mop…mop.*

7. **Find the row marked number 7. Look at the picture. It is a** *hat.* **Look at the three words in the same row. Circle the word** *hat…hat.*

8. **Find the row marked number 8. Look at the picture. It is a** *pot.* **Look at the three words in the same row. Circle the word** *pot…pot.*

9. **Find the row marked number 9. Look at the picture. It is a** *dad.* **Look at the three words in the same row. Circle the word** *dad…dad.*

10. **Find the row marked number 10. Look at the picture. It is a** *lid.* **Look at the three words in the same row. Circle the word** *lid…lid.*

COMPREHENSION

Turn to page 21 and have children look at the picture. Read the questions and all of the answer choices on page 22 aloud to the class.

WRITING

Turn to page 23. Read the prompt and tips aloud to children.

Weekly Test R5

HIGH-FREQUENCY WORDS

Turn to page 25. As you say a word aloud, the child will circle it.

Turn to page 25 in your booklet. I am going to say a word in each row, and you are going to circle the word I am saying.

1. **Find the row marked number 1. Look at the three words. Circle the word *with*…
   with.**

2. **Find the row marked number 2. Look at the three words. Circle the word *three*…
   three.**

3. **Find the row marked number 3. Look at the three words. Circle the word *he*…*he*.**

4. **Find the row marked number 4. Look at the three words. Circle the word *is*…*is*.**

5. **Find the row marked number 5. Look at the three words. Circle the word *to*…*to*.**

WORD READING

Turn to page 26. Children are to circle the word shown in the picture.

Now you are going to circle the word in each row that is shown in the picture.

6. **Find the row marked number 6. Look at the picture. It is a *jet*. Look at the three words in the same row. Circle the word *jet*…*jet*.**

7. **Find the row marked number 7. Look at the picture. It is a *rat*. Look at the three words in the same row. Circle the word *rat*…*rat*.**

8. **Find the row marked number 8. Look at the picture. It is a *bed*. Look at the three words in the same row. Circle the word *bed*…*bed*.**

9. **Find the row marked number 9. Look at the picture. It is a *wig*. Look at the three words in the same row. Circle the word *wig*…*wig*.**

10. **Find the row marked number 10. Look at the picture. It is a *web*. Look at the three words in the same row. Circle the word *web*…*web*.**

COMPREHENSION

Read the questions and answer choices on page 28 aloud to the class.

WRITING

Read the prompt and tips on page 29 aloud to children.

Weekly Test R6

HIGH-FREQUENCY WORDS

Turn to page 31. As you say a word aloud, the child will circle it.

Turn to page 31 in your booklet. I am going to say a word in each row, and you are going to circle the word I am saying.

1. **Find the row marked number 1. Look at the three words. Circle the word** *go…go.*

2. **Find the row marked number 2. Look at the three words. Circle the word** *me…me.*

3. **Find the row marked number 3. Look at the three words. Circle the word** *for…for.*

4. **Find the row marked number 4. Look at the three words. Circle the word** *where…where.*

5. **Find the row marked number 5. Look at the three words. Circle the word** *here…here.*

WORD READING

Turn to page 32. Children are to circle the word shown in the picture.

Turn to page 32 in your booklet. Now you are going to circle the word in each row that is shown in the picture.

6. **Find the row marked number 6. Look at the picture. It is a** *van.* **Look at the three words in the same row. Circle the word** *van…van.*

7. **Find the row marked number 7. Look at the picture. It is a** *bus.* **Look at the three words in the same row. Circle the word** *bus…bus.*

8. **Find the row marked number 8. Look at the picture. It is the** *sun.* **Look at the three words in the same row. Circle the word** *sun…sun.*

9. **Find the row marked number 9. Look at the picture. It is a** *run.* **Look at the three words in the same row. Circle the word** *run…run.*

10. **Find the row marked number 10. Look at the picture. It is a** *bug.* **Look at the three words in the same row. Circle the word** *bug…bug.*

COMPREHENSION

Read the questions and answer choices on page 34 aloud to the class.

WRITING

Read the prompt and tips on page 35 aloud to children.

Name _____

HIGH-FREQUENCY WORDS

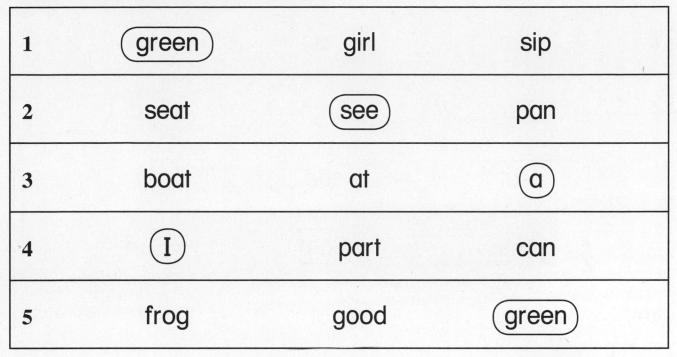

1	(green)	girl	sip
2	seat	(see)	pan
3	boat	at	(a)
4	(I)	part	can
5	frog	good	(green)

Common Core State Standards

Questions 1–5: CCSS Foundational Skills 3.g. Recognize and read grade-appropriate irregularly spelled words.

GO ON

WORD READING

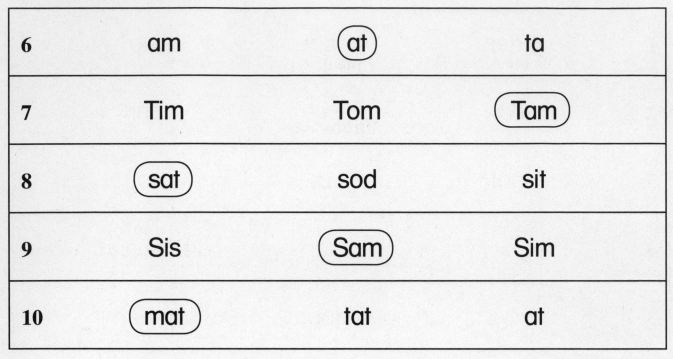

6	am	at	ta
7	Tim	Tom	Tam
8	sat	sod	sit
9	Sis	Sam	Sim
10	mat	tat	at

GO ON

Common Core State Standards

Questions 6–10: CCSS Foundational Skills 3. Know and apply grade-level phonics and word analysis skills in decoding words.

Name _____

COMPREHENSION

Directions
Look at the pictures. Answer the questions that follow.

Jack's Favorite Things

GO ON

Directions

Read each question. Fill in the circle next to the answer.

11 **What does Jack mostly like to do?**

- ○ do chores
- ○ spend his allowance money
- ● play sports

12 **What is one indoor activity that Jack likes to do?**

- ● read stories with Mom at home
- ○ read stories alone at the library
- ○ bake cookies with Grandma

13 **How does Jack feel when he plays table tennis with Dad?**

- ○ scared
- ● happy
- ○ sad

14 **Which of these do you know Jack likes to do?**

- ○ play video games
- ○ play checkers
- ● go swimming

15 **What does Jack like to do with his younger brother Mark?**

- ● play catch
- ○ play table tennis
- ○ read books

GO ON

Common Core State Standards

Questions 11–15: CCSS Literature 7. Use illustrations and details in a story to describe its characters, setting, or events.

Name _____

WRITTEN RESPONSE TO THE SELECTION

Look Back and Write Look back at page 21. Where is Tam?
Write the things you see.

Use the list in the box below to help you as you write.

REMEMBER—YOU SHOULD

☐ tell whcrc Tam is.

☐ tell about the things you see.

☐ try to use correct spelling, capitalization, punctuation, grammar, and sentences.

Common Core State Standards

CCSS Literature 7. Use illustrations and details in a story to describe its characters, setting, or events. (Also **CCSS Literature 1.**, **CCSS Writing 8.**, **CCSS Language 1.**, **CCSS Language 2.**)

Name _____

HIGH-FREQUENCY WORDS

1	kite	(like)	lip
2	work	tip	(we)
3	(the)	math	tea
4	owl	(one)	sun
5	(like)	rake	lap

Common Core State Standards

Questions 1–5: CCSS Foundational Skills 3.g. Recognize and read grade-appropriate irregularly spelled words.

WORD READING

6		car	sat	(cat)
7	(pan image)	(pan)	nap	pat
8	(map image)	mop	man	(map)
9	(can image)	(can)	pat	tan
10	(cap image)	cup	(cap)	tap

GO ON

Common Core State Standards

Questions 6–10: CCSS Foundational Skills 3. Know and apply grade-level phonics and word analysis skills in decoding words.

Name _____

COMPREHENSION

Directions
Look at the picture. Answer the questions that follow.

A Fishing Trip

GO ON

Directions

Read each question. Fill in the circle next to the answer.

11 **Where does this story happen?**
- ○ at a small pond
- ● at a big lake
- ○ at a school

12 **Where is the boat?**
- ● in the water
- ○ on the rocks
- ○ in a bathtub

13 **Where is the lighthouse?**
- ○ in the water
- ○ in the boat
- ● on the land

14 **Where is the fish?**
- ○ in the water
- ● on a fish hook
- ○ in a fish tank

15 **What kind of day is it?**
- ○ snowy
- ○ rainy
- ● sunny

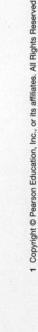

Common Core State Standards

Questions 11–15: CCSS Literature 7. Use illustrations and details in a story to describe its characters, setting, or events.

Name _____

WRITTEN RESPONSE TO THE SELECTION

Look Back and Write Look back at pages 51 and 52. Who comes to Sam's house? Write about what this person does.

Use the list in the box below to help you as you write.

REMEMBER—YOU SHOULD

☐ tell who comes to Sam's house.

☐ tell what this person does.

☐ try to use correct spelling, capitalization, punctuation, grammar, and sentences.

Common Core State Standards

CCSS Literature 7. Use illustrations and details in a story to describe its characters, setting, or events. (Also **CCSS Literature 1.,** **CCSS Literature 3., CCSS Writing 8., CCSS Language 1., CCSS Language 2.**)

Name _____

HIGH-FREQUENCY WORDS

1	coat	(do)	sit
2	(look)	end	book
3	four	pen	(you)
4	(was)	pull	zoo
5	rug	(yellow)	yell

Common Core State Standards

Questions 1–5: CCSS Foundational Skills 3.g. Recognize and read grade-appropriate irregularly spelled words.

WORD READING

6		sat	(pin)	fin
7		ban	big	(bag)
8		(pig)	cap	fig
9		cat	(cab)	bat
10		(fan)	bin	fat

GO ON

Questions 6–10: CCSS Foundational Skills 3.b. Decode regularly spelled one-syllable words.

Name _____

COMPREHENSION

Directions

Look at the pictures. Answer the questions that follow.

Kim's Day

GO ON

Directions

Read each question. Fill in the circle next to the answer.

11 **What does Kim do first?**

- ○ have a snack
- ● wake up
- ○ come home from school

12 **What does Kim do at school during recess?**

- ○ read a book
- ○ ride the school bus
- ● jump rope

13 **Where is Kim at the end of the story?**

- ● in the kitchen
- ○ in her bedroom
- ○ at the playground

14 **What does Kim do after she comes home from school?**

- ○ jump rope
- ○ go to bed
- ● have a snack

15 **What does Kim bring home from school?**

- ○ a dog
- ● a book
- ○ a ball

GO ON

⎛ **Common Core State Standards** ⎞

Questions 11–15: CCSS Literature 7. Use illustrations and details in a story to describe its characters, setting, or events.

Name _____

WRITTEN RESPONSE TO THE SELECTION

Look Back and Write Look back at page 79. Where are Tip and Tam? Write about how you know.

Use the list in the box below to help you as you write.

REMEMBER—YOU SHOULD

☐   tell where Tip and Tam are.

☐   tell how you know where they are.

☐   try to use correct spelling, capitalization, punctuation, grammar, and sentences.

Common Core State Standards

CCSS Literature 7. Use illustrations and details in a story to describe its characters, setting, or events. (Also **CCSS Literature 1.**, **CCSS Literature 3.**, **CCSS Writing 8.**, **CCSS Language 1.**, **CCSS Language 2.**)

Weekly Test R3 Unit R Week 3

Name _____

HIGH-FREQUENCY WORDS

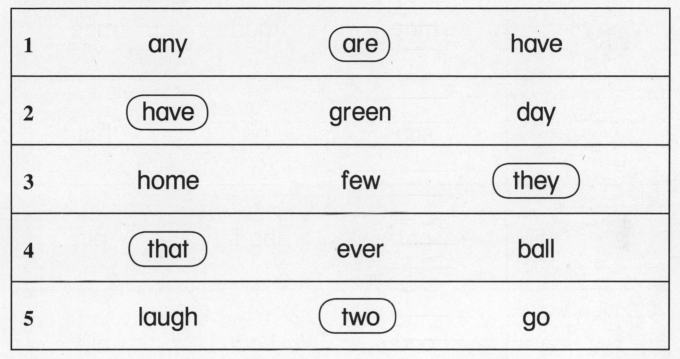

1	any	(are)	have
2	(have)	green	day
3	home	few	(they)
4	(that)	ever	ball
5	laugh	(two)	go

GO ON

Common Core State Standards

Questions 1–5: CCSS Foundational Skills 3.g. Recognize and read grade-appropriate irregularly spelled words.

WORD READING

6	(mop)	mad	map
7	sad	hit	(hat)
8	(pot)	pod	pit
9	(dad)	had	bid
10	bib	(lid)	hit

GO ON

Common Core State Standards

Questions 6–10: CCSS Foundational Skills 3. Know and apply grade-level phonics and word analysis skills in decoding words.

Name _____

COMPREHENSION

Directions
Look at the picture. Answer the questions that follow.

Dave's Birthday Party

GO ON

Directions

Read each question. Fill in the circle next to the answer.

11 **Who can wear a party hat in real life?**

- ● Dave
- ○ the dog
- ○ the frog

12 **How do you know this picture is make-believe?**

- ○ Dave is having a birthday party.
- ○ The cat and dog are friends.
- ● Animals don't go to birthday parties.

13 **What can really happen?**

- ○ Animals can eat and drink like people.
- ○ Animals can blow up balloons and buy presents.
- ● A boy can have a birthday party.

14 **What can happen at a birthday party?**

- ○ Animals give people presents.
- ● People sing "Happy Birthday."
- ○ Animals sing "Happy Birthday."

15 **What cannot be real?**

- ○ the candles on the birthday cake
- ○ the bows and wrapping paper on the presents
- ● the animals sitting at the table with Dave

GO ON

Common Core State Standards

Questions 11–15: CCSS Literature 3. Describe characters, settings, and major events in a story, using key details.

Name _____

WRITTEN RESPONSE TO THE SELECTION

Look Back and Write Look back at pages 98 and 99. What do Pam and Dot like to do? Write about it.

Use the list in the box below to help you as you write.

REMEMBER—YOU SHOULD

☐   tell what Pam and Dot like to do.

☐   use your best handwriting.

☐   try to use correct spelling, capitalization, punctuation, grammar, and sentences.

Common Core State Standards

CCSS Literature 7. Use illustrations and details in a story to describe its characters, setting, or events. (Also **CCSS Literature 1.**, **CCSS Literature 3.**, **CCSS Writing 8.**, **CCSS Language 1.**, **CCSS Language 2.**)

Name _____

HIGH-FREQUENCY WORDS

1	teeth	went	⬭ with ⬭
2	the	⬭ three ⬭	path
3	⬭ he ⬭	help	she
4	⬭ is ⬭	slip	wish
5	ten	not	⬭ to ⬭

Common Core State Standards

Questions 1–5: CCSS Foundational Skills 3.g. Recognize and read grade-appropriate irregularly spelled words.

WORD READING

6	jam	ten	(jet)
7	cot	(rat)	fat
8	(bed)	fed	bet
9	leg	(wig)	win
10	wet	lid	(web)

GO ON

Common Core State Standards

Questions 6–10: CCSS Foundational Skills 3.b. Decode regularly spelled one-syllable words.

Name _____

COMPREHENSION

Directions
Look at the pictures. Answer the questions that follow.

Pete's Toy Boat

1.
2.
3.
4.

GO ON

irections

Read each question. Fill in the circle next to the answer.

11 **What happens first?**

- ○ Pete sails his boat.
- ● Pete builds and paints his boat.
- ○ Pete and Dad go to the park.

12 **What happens in picture 2?**

- ○ Pete and Dad decide what to have for dinner.
- ○ Dad gives Pete his old model boat to play with.
- ● Pete asks Dad where they can sail his boat.

13 **How do Pete and Dad get to the park?**

- ● They walk there.
- ○ They drive there.
- ○ They take a bus there.

14 **Where do Pete and Dad sail the boat?**

- ○ in the bathtub
- ● in a pond
- ○ in the ocean

15 **Where are Pete and Dad at the end of the story?**

- ○ at school
- ● in the park
- ○ at home

Common Core State Standards

Questions 11–15: CCSS Literature 3. Describe characters, settings, and major events in a story, using key details.

Name _____

WRITTEN RESPONSE TO THE SELECTION

Look Back and Write Look back at page 128. What will Kim, Jill, and Pat do?

Use the list in the box below to help you as you write.

REMEMBER—YOU SHOULD

☐ tell what Kim, Jill, and Pat will do.

☐ look at the picture to see what they will do.

☐ try to use correct spelling, capitalization, punctuation, grammar, and sentences.

Common Core State Standards

CCSS Literature 7. Use illustrations and details in a story to describe its characters, setting, or events. (Also **CCSS Literature 1.**, **CCSS Literature 3.**, **CCSS Writing 8.**, **CCSS Language 1.**, **CCSS Language 2.**)

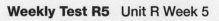

Name _____

HIGH-FREQUENCY WORDS

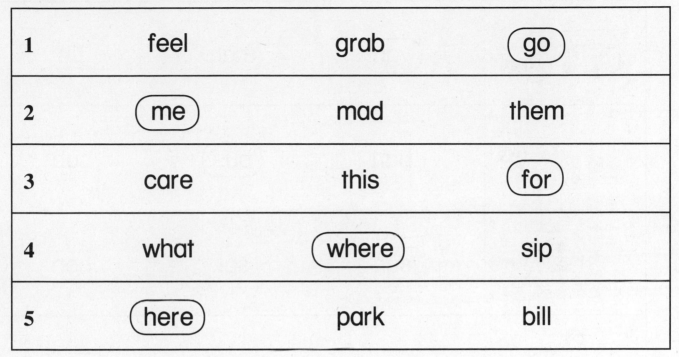

1	feel	grab	(go)
2	(me)	mad	them
3	care	this	(for)
4	what	(where)	sip
5	(here)	park	bill

GO ON

Common Core State Standards

Questions 1–5: CCSS Foundational Skills 3.g. Recognize and read grade-appropriate irregularly spelled words.

WORD READING

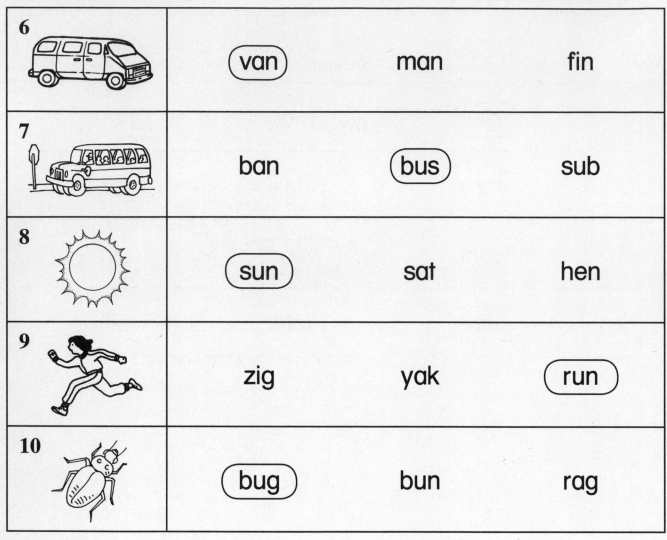

6	(van)	man	fin
7	ban	(bus)	sub
8	(sun)	sat	hen
9	zig	yak	(run)
10	(bug)	bun	rag

GO ON

Common Core State Standards

Questions 6–10: CCSS Foundational Skills 3. Know and apply grade-level phonics and word analysis skills in decoding words.

Name _____

COMPREHENSION

Directions

Look at the picture. Answer the questions that follow.

Out for a Walk

GO ON

Directions

Read each question. Fill in the circle next to the answer.

11 **What can really happen?**

- ● A lady can walk a dog.
- ○ Fish can walk.
- ○ Fish can breathe on land.

12 **What is make-believe?**

- ○ People walk down sidewalks.
- ○ Babies are pushed in strollers.
- ● Fish wear clothes.

13 **What is Mr. Fish doing in the picture?**

- ○ waving to his baby
- ● waving to the lady
- ○ waving to the dog

14 **What could Mr. and Mrs. Fish do in real life?**

- ○ wave to a person on land
- ● swim in the water
- ○ put their baby in a stroller and go for a walk

15 **What could you change to make this picture real?**

- ● change Mr. and Mrs. Fish to people
- ○ change the lady to a fish
- ○ change where it is happening to be under water

GO ON

Common Core State Standards

Questions 11–15: CCSS Literature 5. Explain major differences between books that tell stories and books that give information, drawing on a wide reading of a range of text types.

Name _____

WRITTEN RESPONSE TO THE SELECTION

Look Back and Write Look back at page 155. What can you buy at a farmers market? Write about it.

Use the list in the box below to help you as you write.

REMEMBER—YOU SHOULD

☐   tell about what you can buy at a farmers market.

☐   look at the picture to see what you can buy at a farmers market.

☐   try to use correct spelling, capitalization, punctuation, grammar, and sentences.

GO ON

Common Core State Standards

CCSS Literature 7. Use illustrations and details in a story to describe its characters, setting, or events. (Also **CCSS Literature 1.,** **CCSS Literature 3., CCSS Writing 8., CCSS Language 1., CCSS Language 2.)**

Name _____

HIGH-FREQUENCY WORDS

Directions
Fill in the circle next to the word that fills the blank.

1 Will you _____ to dinner?

- ○ he
- ○ do
- ● come

2 The man ran that _____.

- ● way
- ○ with
- ○ are

3 The cat sat on _____ lap.

- ● my
- ○ for
- ○ to

4 She sits _____ her room.

- ○ two
- ● in
- ○ at

5 I do not see Texas _____ the map.

- ○ that
- ○ are
- ● on

GO ON

Common Core State Standards

Questions 1–5: CCSS Foundational Skills 3.g. Recognize and read grade-appropriate irregularly spelled words.

PHONICS

Directions
Fill in the circle next to the answer.

6 The <u>cat</u> sleeps on the chair.

Which word has the same sound as the <u>a</u> in <u>cat</u>?

- ● mat
- ○ ate
- ○ March

7 I <u>am</u> Pat.

Which word has the same sound as the <u>a</u> in <u>am</u>?

- ● jam
- ○ late
- ○ are

8 School gets out <u>at</u> three.

Which word has the same sound as the <u>a</u> in <u>at</u>?

- ○ then
- ○ what
- ● hat

9 The <u>back</u> door is open.

Which word has the same sound as the <u>ck</u> in <u>back</u>?

- ● sack
- ○ short
- ○ bad

10 The car is <u>black</u>.

Which word has the same sound as the <u>ck</u> in <u>black</u>?

- ○ chair
- ● jack
- ○ glad

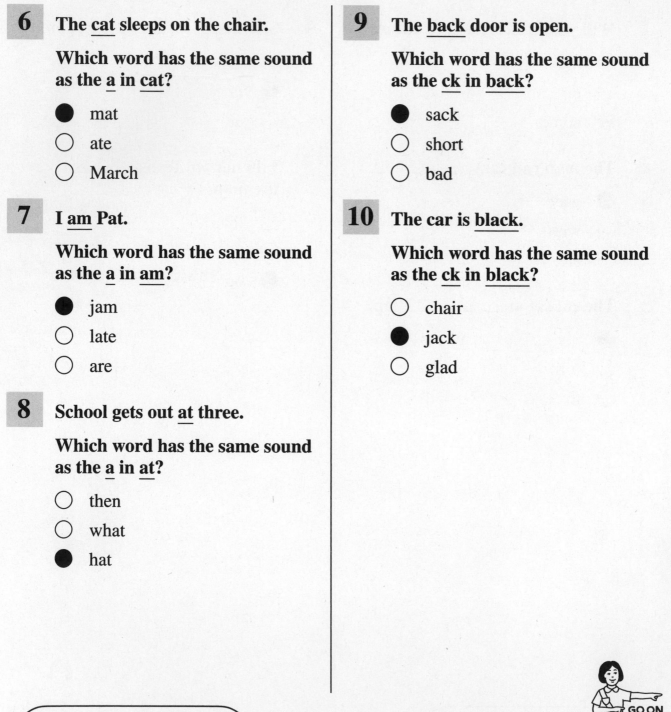

GO ON

Common Core State Standards

Questions 6–10: CCSS Foundational Skills 3. Know and apply grade-level phonics and word analysis skills in decoding words.

Name _____

COMPREHENSION

Pam and Jack

Pam has a cat. The cat is Jack. Jack is a pal.

Pam has a tan van.

Jack can nap on a mat in the van.

GO ON

Directions
Fill in the circle next to the answer.

11 What does Pam have?

○ a dog

● a cat

○ a bird

12 What is the cat's name?

● Jack

○ Sam

○ Pam

13 What does Pam have?

○ a can

○ a ball

● a van

14 What color is the van?

○ green

○ yellow

● tan

15 What does Jack do in the van?

○ eats fish

○ plays with a ball

● naps on a mat

GO ON

Common Core State Standards

Questions 11–15: CCSS Literature 3. Describe characters, settings, and major events in a story, using key details.

Name _____

WRITTEN RESPONSE TO THE SELECTION

Look Back and Write Look back at page 25. Where does Sam run first? Write about it.

Use the list in the box below to help you as you write.

REMEMBER—YOU SHOULD

☐ tell where Sam runs first.

☐ tell why you think he runs there.

☐ try to use correct spelling, capitalization, punctuation, grammar, and sentences.

Common Core State Standards

CCSS Literature 3. Describe characters, settings, and major events in a story, using key details. (Also **CCSS Literature 1.**, **CCSS Literature 7.**, **CCSS Writing 8.**, **CCSS Language 1.**, **CCSS Language 2.**)

Name _____

HIGH-FREQUENCY WORDS

Directions
Fill in the circle next to the word that fills the blank.

1 _____ the cup from the table.

- ○ While
- ● Take
- ○ Two

2 Look at Pat and Tim go _____.

- ○ like
- ○ they
- ● up

3 _____ is the dog's name?

- ○ Up
- ● What
- ○ Run

4 _____ plays with a doll.

- ○ Door
- ● She
- ○ Six

5 _____ are you wearing?

- ● What
- ○ Am
- ○ They

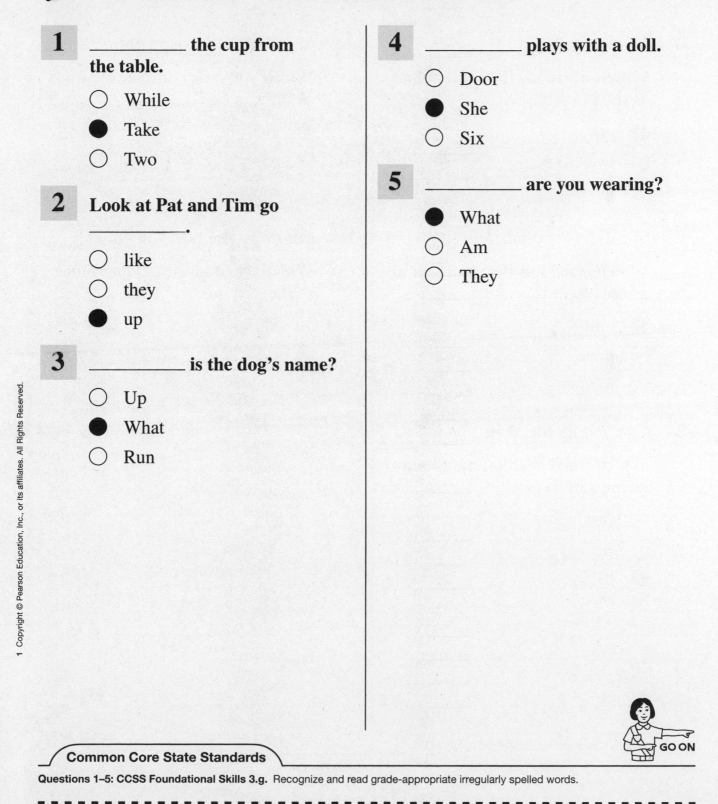

GO ON

Common Core State Standards

Questions 1–5: CCSS Foundational Skills 3.g. Recognize and read grade-appropriate irregularly spelled words.

PHONICS

Directions
Fill in the circle next to the answer.

6 I have a gold <u>pin</u>.

Which word has the same sound as the <u>i</u> in <u>pin</u>?

● pig
○ frog
○ pine

7 She <u>did</u> a good job.

Which word has the same sound as the <u>i</u> in <u>did</u>?

● him
○ mine
○ my

8 Can you <u>fix</u> the chair?

Which word has the same sound as the <u>x</u> in <u>fix</u>?

○ fits
○ fizz
● tricks

9 My sister is <u>six</u> years old.

Which word has the same sound as the <u>x</u> in <u>six</u>?

● kicks
○ pick
○ stick

10 Put down the <u>box</u>.

Which word has the same sound as the <u>x</u> in <u>box</u>?

○ hot
● sacks
○ mats

GO ON

> Common Core State Standards

Questions 6–10: CCSS Language 2.d. Use conventional spelling for words with common spelling patterns and for frequently occurring irregular words.

Name _____

COMPREHENSION

A Sad Pal

Pat, Jan, Rick, and Jim are pals.

Pat can bat with Jan and Rick.

Pat can dig with Jan and Rick.

Where is Jim?

Jim is sick.

Jim is a sad pal!

Directions

Fill in the circle next to the answer.

11 Pat can bat with _____ .

- ○ Jim
- ● Jan and Rick
- ○ Jan, Rick, and Jim

12 Pat can not bat with _____ .

- ○ Jan
- ○ Rick
- ● Jim

13 Pat can _____ with Jan and Rick.

- ● dig
- ○ play
- ○ sit

14 Pat can not dig with _____ .

- ○ Jan
- ○ Rick
- ● Jim

15 Jim is _____ .

- ○ green
- ○ here
- ● sick

GO ON

Common Core State Standards

Questions 11–15: CCSS Literature 3. Describe characters, settings, and major events in a story, using key details.

Weekly Test 2 Unit 1 Week 2

Name _____

WRITTEN RESPONSE TO THE SELECTION

Look Back and Write Look back at page 57. How does Pig feel? Write about it. Use evidence from the story.

Use the list in the box below to help you as you write.

REMEMBER—YOU SHOULD

☐   tell how Pig feels.

☐   tell how you know.

☐   try to use correct spelling, capitalization, punctuation, grammar, and sentences.

Common Core State Standards

CCSS Literature 3. Describe characters, settings, and major events in a story, using key details. (Also **CCSS Literature 1.**, **CCSS Literature 7.**, **CCSS Writing 8.**, **CCSS Language 1.**, **CCSS Language 2.**)

Weekly Test 2 Unit 1 Week 2

Name _____

HIGH-FREQUENCY WORDS

Directions
Fill in the circle next to the word that fills the blank.

1 Max had two _____ socks.
- ● blue
- ○ rake
- ○ go

2 A doctor will _____ him.
- ○ little
- ○ for
- ● help

3 They _____ the car.
- ○ was
- ● use
- ○ with

4 My _____ brother is crying.
- ● little
- ○ from
- ○ and

5 Mike takes the bone _____ the dog.
- ○ am
- ○ where
- ● from

GO ON

1 Copyright © Pearson Education, Inc., or its affiliates. All Rights Reserved.

Common Core State Standards

Questions 1–5: CCSS Foundational Skills 3.g. Recognize and read grade-appropriate irregularly spelled words.

PHONICS

Directions
Fill in the circle next to the word that fills the blank.

6 How many _____ does she have?

   ○ catz

   ○ cat

   ● cats

7 I have four red _____.

   ● pens

   ○ pen

   ○ penz

8 We have two _____.

   ○ dog

   ● dogs

   ○ dogz

Directions
Fill in the circle next to the answer.

9 I found a <u>rock</u>.

Which word has the same sound as the <u>o</u> in <u>rock</u>?

   ○ boot

   ● not

   ○ you

10 The frog can <u>hop</u>.

Which word has the same sound as the <u>o</u> in <u>hop</u>?

   ● lock

   ○ pole

   ○ door

GO ON

Common Core State Standards

Questions 6–10: CCSS Foundational Skills 3.b. Decode regularly spelled one-syllable words.

Name _____

COMPREHENSION

Socks in a Box

Rob has a job. His job is at the dock.

His job is to pack.

Rob can pack a big box. The box has socks in it.

Rob is hot. What a lot of socks!

Rob, take the box of socks to Bill.

You can sit, Rob.

GO ON

Directions

Fill in the circle next to the answer.

11 **Where does Rob work?**

- ○ on a farm
- ● at the dock
- ○ at a school

12 **What is Rob's job?**

- ○ He packs a big box with pots.
- ● He packs a big box with socks.
- ○ He packs a big box with pans.

13 **Who does Rob take the box to?**

- ○ Jan
- ○ Mom
- ● Bill

14 **How does Rob feel?**

- ○ happy
- ○ sad
- ● hot

15 **What can Rob do at the end of the story?**

- ○ run
- ● sit
- ○ nap

Common Core State Standards

Questions 11–15: CCSS Literature 3. Describe characters, settings, and major events in a story, using key details.

Name _____

WRITTEN RESPONSE TO THE SELECTION

Look Back and Write Look back at pages 79–82. Write some things Ox can do to help. Be sure to use evidence from the story.

Use the list in the box below to help you as you write.

REMEMBER—YOU SHOULD

☐ tell what Ox can do to help.

☐ tell what you see in the pictures.

☐ try to use correct spelling, capitalization, punctuation, grammar, and sentences.

Common Core State Standards

CCSS Literature 3. Describe characters, settings, and major events in a story, using key details. (Also **CCSS Literature 1.**, **CCSS Literature 7.**, **CCSS Writing 8.**, **CCSS Language 1.**, **CCSS Language 2.**)

Name _____

HIGH-FREQUENCY WORDS

Directions

Fill in the circle next to the word that fills the blank.

1 It is time to _____ dinner.

- ◯ on
- ● eat
- ◯ the

2 She is _____ feet tall.

- ● four
- ◯ am
- ◯ on

3 I have _____ toes on my foot.

- ● five
- ◯ ball
- ◯ in

4 Let's read _____ book.

- ● this
- ◯ blue
- ◯ desk

5 Can you come _____?

- ◯ her
- ● too
- ◯ say

GO ON

Common Core State Standards

Questions 1–5: CCSS Foundational Skills 3.g. Recognize and read grade-appropriate irregularly spelled words.

PHONICS

Directions
Fill in the circle next to the word that fills the blank.

6 The dog is _____ outside.
- ● running
- ○ run
- ○ runs

7 The baby _____ all day.
- ○ rock
- ● rocks
- ○ rocking

8 He is _____ on the box.
- ○ jump
- ○ jumps
- ● jumping

9 We are _____ cake.
- ○ eat
- ○ eats
- ● eating

10 Dan _____ down the hall.
- ○ look
- ● looks
- ○ looking

GO ON

Common Core State Standards

Questions 6–10: CCSS Foundational Skills 3.f. Read words with inflectional endings.

Name _____

COMPREHENSION

Kit Cat

Kit is my pet cat.

Kit runs a lot. Look at Kit run!

Where is Kit? Kit ran in a bag.

Kit gets a hat. Kit rips it. Bad cat!

Kit naps a lot. Kit naps on a big, red sack.

Kit can eat a lot. Kit will eat her dinner.

Directions

Fill in the circle next to the best answer.

11 **What is this story about?**

- ○ a girl
- ● a cat
- ○ a fly

12 **What does Kit play in?**

- ● a bag
- ○ water
- ○ a tree

13 **What does Kit like to do?**

- ○ She likes to lick.
- ● She likes to nap.
- ○ She likes to sit.

14 **What does Kit do to the hat?**

- ○ She licks the hat.
- ○ She eats the hat.
- ● She rips the hat.

15 **What is another good name for this story?**

- ○ Sad Kit
- ○ Sick Kit
- ● Pet Kit

GO ON

Common Core State Standards

Questions 11–15: CCSS Informational Text 2. Identify the main topic and retell key details of a text.

Name _____

WRITTEN RESPONSE TO THE SELECTION

Look Back and Write Look back at page 109. Write about how the fox takes care of her kit. Use evidence from the selection.

Use the list in the box below to help you as you write.

REMEMBER—YOU SHOULD

☐ tell how the fox takes care of her kit.

☐ tell how you know.

☐ try to use correct spelling, capitalization, punctuation, grammar, and sentences.

⎛ **Common Core State Standards** ⎞

CCSS Informational Text 3. Describe the connection between two individuals, events, ideas, or pieces of information in a text.
(Also **CCSS Informational Text 2., CCSS Informational Text 7., CCSS Writing 2., CCSS Language 1., CCSS Language 2.**)

Name _____

HIGH-FREQUENCY WORDS

Directions
Fill in the circle next to the word that fills the blank.

1 He _____ a fox.
- ○ this
- ○ for
- ● saw

2 The cat sat in the _____.
- ● tree
- ○ too
- ○ take

3 _____ mom is calling you.
- ○ Ball
- ● Your
- ○ New

4 The house is _____.
- ○ from
- ● small
- ○ what

5 I have _____ sled.
- ○ come
- ○ up
- ● your

GO ON

⌐ **Common Core State Standards** ⌐

Questions 1–5: CCSS Foundational Skills 3.g. Recognize and read grade-appropriate irregularly spelled words.

PHONICS

Directions
Fill in the circle next to the answer.

6 Water is cold and <u>wet</u>.

Which word has the same sound as the <u>e</u> in <u>wet</u>?

- ● red
- ○ week
- ○ wild

7 The pencil is <u>yellow</u>.

Which word has the same sound as the <u>e</u> in <u>yellow</u>?

- ○ the
- ● hen
- ○ water

8 The <u>steps</u> are high.

Which word has the same beginning sound as the <u>st</u> in <u>steps</u>?

- ○ seed
- ○ mess
- ● star

9 I have a new <u>black</u> sled.

Which word has the same beginning sound as the <u>bl</u> in <u>black</u>?

- ● blue
- ○ bank
- ○ bun

10 Cut the <u>stem</u> of the flower.

Which word has the same beginning sound as the <u>st</u> in <u>stem</u>?

- ○ hem
- ○ spell
- ● still

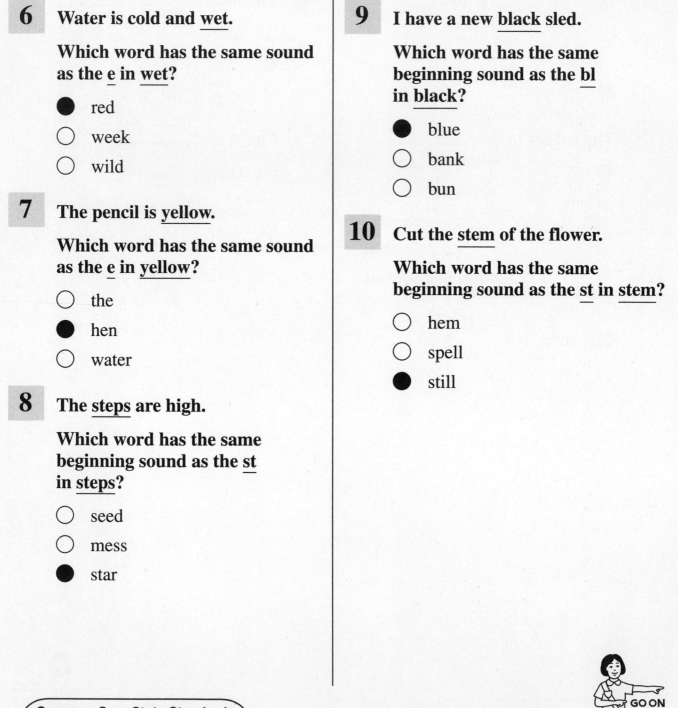

GO ON

Common Core State Standards

Questions 6–10: **CCSS Foundational Skills 3.** Know and apply grade-level phonics and word analysis skills in decoding words.

Name _____

COMPREHENSION

Pet Pals

Dan has pet pals. Nan is a big, red cat. Cass is a small, black bird.

Dan and Nan can play. Dan and Nan run.

Cass can sit on a sill. Cass can see her pals.

Dan gets snacks.

Cass eats well. Good pet, Cass! Nan eats well. Good pet, Nan!

The pet pals nap.

GO ON

Directions

Fill in the circle next to the answer.

11 What is this story about?

- ● a boy and his pets
- ○ a pet that runs
- ○ a pet that sits on a sill

12 What is another good title for this story?

- ○ Pets Can Run Fast
- ○ All Pets Like Snacks
- ● Dan, Nan, and Cass Are Pals

13 What is the name of the big, red cat?

- ○ Dan
- ● Nan
- ○ Cass

14 What does Dan get for the pets?

- ○ some toys
- ○ some birds
- ● some snacks

15 What happens at the end of the story?

- ○ The pets eat.
- ● The pets nap.
- ○ The pets play.

GO ON

⌐ **Common Core State Standards** ⌐

Questions 11–15: CCSS Literature 3. Describe characters, settings, and major events in a story, using key details.

Name _____

WRITTEN RESPONSE TO THE SELECTION

Look Back and Write Look back at pages 134 and 135. Write about how Brad and Kim save the red bird's egg. Provide evidence from the story.

Use the list in the box below to help you as you write.

REMEMBER—YOU SHOULD

 tell how Brad and Kim save the egg.

 use examples from the story.

☐ try to use correct spelling, capitalization, punctuation, grammar, and sentences.

GO ON

Common Core State Standards

CCSS Literature 3. Describe characters, settings, and major events in a story, using key details. (Also **CCSS Literature 1.**, **CCSS Literature 7.**, **CCSS Writing 8.**, **CCSS Language 1.**, **CCSS Language 2.**)

Name _____

HIGH-FREQUENCY WORDS

Directions
Fill in the circle next to the word that fills the blank.

1 Anne runs _____.
- ● home
- ○ and
- ○ the

2 I sat with _____ under a tree.
- ● them
- ○ on
- ○ take

3 How _____ pets do you have?
- ○ far
- ○ bell
- ● many

4 The cat ran _____ the sack.
- ○ am
- ○ way
- ● into

5 We see _____ trees.
- ○ can
- ● many
- ○ help

GO ON

Common Core State Standards
Questions 1–5: CCSS Foundational Skills 3.g. Recognize and read grade-appropriate irregularly spelled words.

PHONICS

Directions
Fill in the circle next to the answer.

6 The room has a red <u>rug</u>.

Which word has the same sound as the <u>u</u> in <u>rug</u>?

- ● duck
- ○ class
- ○ cute

7 Pam got on the <u>bus</u>.

Which word has the same sound as the <u>u</u> in <u>bus</u>?

- ○ bat
- ○ cube
- ● lump

8 I made a shopping <u>list</u>.

Which word has the same final sound as the <u>st</u> in <u>list</u>?

- ○ tent
- ● best
- ○ pond

9 See Dan <u>jump</u>!

Which word has the same final sound as the <u>mp</u> in <u>jump</u>?

- ○ jet
- ○ must
- ● lamp

10 Dan runs <u>fast</u>.

Which word has the same final sound as the <u>st</u> in <u>fast</u>?

- ○ fat
- ○ still
- ● just

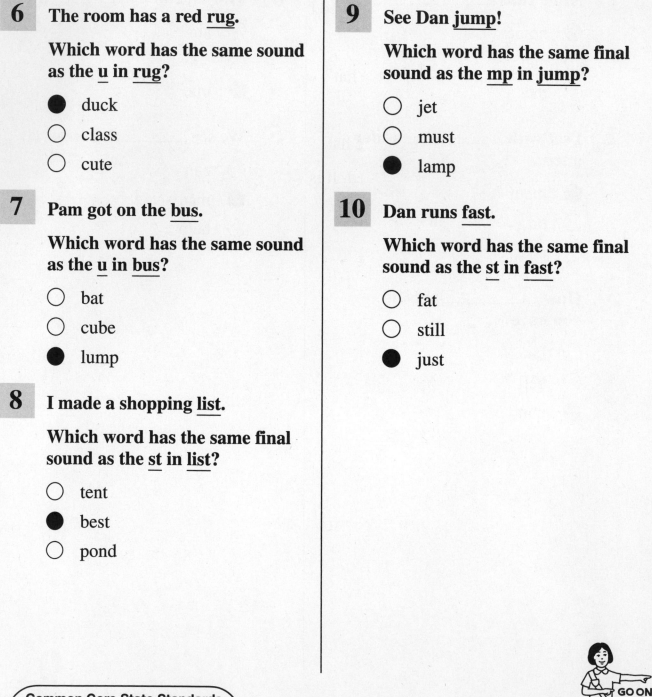

GO ON

Common Core State Standards

Questions 6–10: CCSS Language 2.d. Use conventional spelling for words with common spelling patterns and for frequently occurring irregular words.

Name _____

COMPREHENSION

The Red Hat

Where did Pat set his red hat? Pat must look.

Cat, sit still. Can you help get the red hat?

Cat can not help Pat.

Hen, stop! Can you help get the hat?

Hen can not.

The animals can not help get the hat.

Pat can see a hat! But it is not red. It is a tan hat.

Get Jill. It is her tan hat.

GO ON

Directions

Fill in the circle next to the answer.

11 **Why must Pat look for the hat?**

- ○ The hat is red.
- ○ The hat is with the animals.
- ● The hat is lost.

12 **What does Pat ask the animals?**

- ○ Why did you take the hat?
- ● Can you help find the hat?
- ○ Can you stop and sit still?

13 **What does Pat see?**

- ○ a red hat
- ● a tan hat
- ○ a blue hat

14 **What does Pat say when he sees the tan hat?**

- ○ Give me the hat.
- ○ I must find my hat.
- ● Get Jill.

15 **Who does the tan hat belong to?**

- ○ the cat
- ● Jill
- ○ Pat

GO ON

Common Core State Standards

Questions 11–15: CCSS Informational Text 7. Use the illustrations and details in a text to describe its key ideas.

Name _____

WRITTEN RESPONSE TO THE SELECTION

Look Back and Write Look back at the photographs in the selection. Choose an animal that was in the big park. Use facts from the selection to write about the animal you choose.

Use the list in the box below to help you as you write.

REMEMBER—YOU SHOULD

☐   tell about an animal in the photographs.

☐   use facts from the story.

☐   try to use correct spelling, capitalization, punctuation, grammar, and sentences.

Common Core State Standards

CCSS Writing 2. Write informative/explanatory texts in which they name a topic, supply some facts about the topic, and provide some sense of closure. (Also **CCSS Informational Text 6., CCSS Informational Text 7., CCSS Language 1., CCSS Language 2.**)

Name _____

HIGH-FREQUENCY WORDS

Directions
Fill in the circle next to the word that fills the blank.

1 He wants to _____ a fish.

○ small

● catch

○ said

2 This is a _____ way home.

● good

○ what

○ for

3 She has _____ socks.

○ and

○ up

● no

4 Mom will _____ the ball back.

○ said

● put

○ eat

5 I _____ to go home.

● want

○ take

○ tree

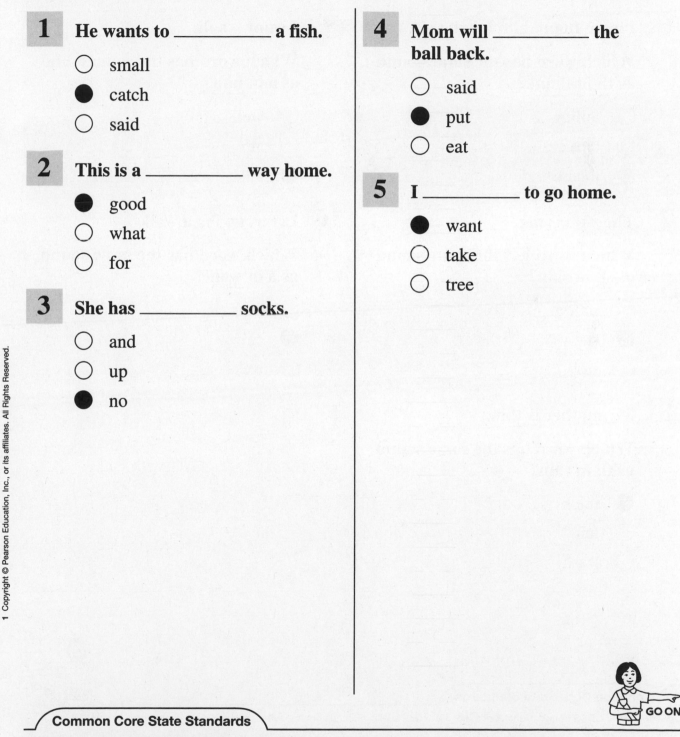

GO ON

Common Core State Standards

Questions 1–5: CCSS Foundational Skills 3.g. Recognize and read grade-appropriate irregularly spelled words.

PHONICS

Directions
Fill in the circle next to the answer.

6 Please <u>thank</u> him for the gift.

Which word has the same sound as <u>th</u> in <u>thank</u>?

○ telling
○ taps
● theme

7 The <u>ship</u> is big.

Which word has the same sound as <u>sh</u> in <u>ship</u>?

○ school
● show
○ stop

8 My mother is <u>thin</u>.

Which word has the same sound as <u>th</u> in <u>thin</u>?

● thick
○ ten
○ trash

9 I want a <u>ball</u>.

Which word has the same sound as <u>a</u> in <u>ball</u>?

○ well
○ am
● talk

10 Let us go for a <u>walk</u>.

Which word has the same sound as <u>a</u> in <u>walk</u>?

○ look
● call
○ was

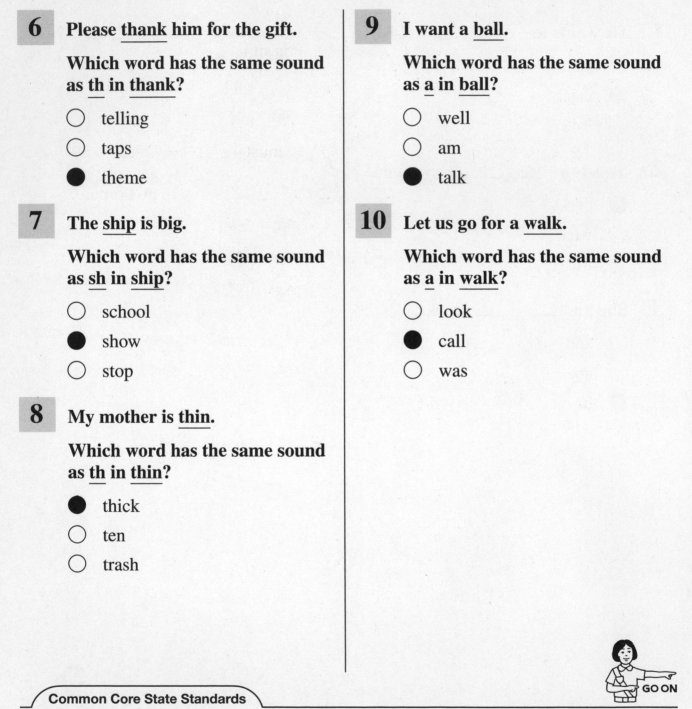

GO ON

Common Core State Standards

Questions 6–8: **CCSS Foundational Skills 3.a.** Know the spelling-sound correspondences for common consonant digraphs.
Questions 9–10: **CCSS Language 2.d.** Use conventional spelling for words with common spelling patterns and for frequently occurring irregular words.

Name _____

COMPREHENSION

The Nest

Matt and Sam go for a walk.

Matt spots a nest in a bush. What is in the nest?

A black bird sits in the nest. Small black birds sit in the nest.

The small birds eat a lot. Then they rest.

Sam spots a cat.

No! Matt and Sam must help the birds. They must stop the cat.

GO ON

Directions

Fill in the circle next to the answer.

11 What do Matt and Sam do at the beginning of the story?

- ○ swim
- ● go for a walk
- ○ play ball

12 What does Matt spot in the bush?

- ○ a mitt
- ● a nest
- ○ a cat

13 What happens after the small birds eat a lot?

- ○ They get big.
- ○ They fly away.
- ● They rest.

14 What does Sam spot?

- ● a cat
- ○ a nest
- ○ a black bird

15 What happens at the end of the story?

- ○ Matt and Sam take the birds.
- ● Matt and Sam stop the cat.
- ○ Matt and Sam run away.

GO ON

Common Core State Standards

Questions 11–15: CCSS Literature 3. Describe characters, settings, and major events in a story, using key details.

Name _____

WRITTEN RESPONSE TO THE SELECTION

Look Back and Write Look back at pages 30 and 31. Where does Max get the big fish? Write about it. Use evidence from the story to support your answer.

Use the list in the box below to help you as you write.

REMEMBER—YOU SHOULD

☐ tell where Max gets a fish.

☐ use examples from the story.

☐ try to use correct spelling, capitalization, punctuation, grammar, and sentences.

Common Core State Standards

CCSS Writing 2. Write informative/explanatory texts in which they name a topic, supply some facts about the topic, and provide some sense of closure. (Also **CCSS Writing 8., CCSS Language 1., CCSS Language 2.**)

Name _____

HIGH-FREQUENCY WORDS

Directions
Fill in the circle next to the word that fills the blank.

1 She will not _____ mad.

- ○ of
- ○ up
- ● be

2 I _____ go to the park.

- ○ home
- ● could
- ○ good

3 The _____ is big.

- ● horse
- ○ for
- ○ have

4 The farmer has an _____ truck.

- ○ many
- ● old
- ○ want

5 Can I have this _____?

- ○ small
- ○ from
- ● paper

Common Core State Standards

Questions 1–5: **CCSS Foundational Skills 3.g.** Recognize and read grade-appropriate irregularly spelled words.

PHONICS

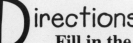irections

Fill in the circle next to the answer.

6 She woke up <u>late</u>.

Which word has the same sound
as the <u>a</u> in late?

● name
○ ran
○ hat

7 I am <u>safe</u>.

Which word has the same sound
as <u>a</u> in safe?

○ had
○ five
● made

8 I can read the <u>page</u>.

Which word has the same sound
as <u>a</u> in page?

○ here
○ that
● age

9 She will win the <u>race</u>.

Which word has the same sound
as <u>a</u> in race?

○ rat
● lake
○ eat

10 He is <u>nice</u>.

Which word has the same sound
as <u>c</u> in nice?

○ can
● ice
○ car

GO ON

Common Core State Standards

Questions 6–9: CCSS Foundational Skills 3.c. Know final -e and common vowel team conventions for representing long vowel sounds.
Question 10: CCSS Language 2.d. Use conventional spelling for words with common spelling patterns and for frequently occurring irregular words.

80

Weekly Test 8 Unit 2 Week 2

Name _____

COMPREHENSION

Name the Plant

Mom is sick. Dad gave Mom a plant. What is the plant?

Dad can not tell. Mom can not tell.

Dad puts the plant in a pot. Then he puts it in the sun.

The plant gets big. But what is the plant?

Dad and Mom still can not tell.

It is a sad plant with no name. Let us name it. We will call the plant Jane.

GO ON

Directions

Fill in the circle next to the answer.

11 **Dad gave Mom a plant. Why?**

- ○ She helped him.
- ● She is sick.
- ○ She loves plants.

12 **What does Dad do next?**

- ○ He names the plant.
- ○ He digs a hole for the plant.
- ● He puts the plant in a pot.

13 **Why does Dad put the plant in the sun?**

- ● It will grow.
- ○ It will get green.
- ○ It will get a name.

14 **Why is the plant sad?**

- ● It has no name.
- ○ It can not grow.
- ○ It is sick.

15 **What happens when they do not know what kind of plant it is?**

- ○ They take the plant back to the store.
- ● The family gives the plant a name.
- ○ Everyone tries to guess what kind of plant it is.

Common Core State Standards

Questions 11–15: **CCSS Literature 1.** Ask and answer questions about key details in a text.

Name _____

WRITTEN RESPONSE TO THE SELECTION

Look Back and Write Look back at pages 60–63. Write about an actor in the play. Use evidence in the selection to support your answer.

Use the list in the box below to help you as you write.

REMEMBER—YOU SHOULD

☐ write about an actor in the play.

☐ use examples from the story in your answer.

☐ try to use correct spelling, capitalization, punctuation, grammar, and sentences.

Common Core State Standards

CCSS Writing 2. Write informative/explanatory texts in which they name a topic, supply some facts about the topic, and provide some sense of closure. (Also **CCSS Writing 8.**, **CCSS Language 1.**, **CCSS Language 2.**)

Name _____

HIGH-FREQUENCY WORDS

Directions
Fill in the circle next to the word that fills the blank.

1 I _____ in town.
- ● live
- ○ her
- ○ many

2 _____ has the ball?
- ○ Where
- ○ Up
- ● Who

3 The _____ are happy.
- ○ look
- ● people
- ○ from

4 He will take the dog _____.
- ○ tell
- ○ them
- ● out

5 They _____ in the factory.
- ● work
- ○ tree
- ○ little

GO ON

Common Core State Standards

Questions 1–5: **CCSS Foundational Skills 3.g.** Recognize and read grade-appropriate irregularly spelled words.

PHONICS

irections
Fill in the circle next to the answer.

6 I like horses.

Which word has the same sound as the i in like?

● time
○ big
○ this

7 We went for a ride.

Which word has the same sound as the i in ride?

○ which
○ bird
● bike

8 Who is at the door?

Which word has the same sound as the wh in who?

○ she
● whole
○ them

9 I don't know which toy to choose.

Which word has the same sound as the ch in choose?

○ could
● child
○ yellow

10 My teacher wears a watch.

Which word has the same sound as the tch in watch?

● catch
○ horse
○ race

GO ON

Common Core State Standards

Questions 6–7: CCSS Foundational Skills 3.c. Know final -e and common vowel team conventions for representing long vowel sounds.
Questions 8–10: CCSS Foundational Skills 3.a. Know the spelling-sound correspondences for common consonant digraphs.

Name _____

COMPREHENSION

Where Is Mop?

Dan has a black pup, Mop. Mop likes to run all the time.

Mop makes Dan smile.

Mop takes a cap and runs with it. Stop, Mop!

Where is Mop? Dan can not see her. Did Mop hide?

Is this a game, Mop? No!

Mop is stuck. Dan can help her.

That was bad, Mop!

GO ON

Directions

Fill in the circle next to the answer.

11 **What does Mop like to do?**

○ sit and nap

● run all the time

○ get stuck

12 **What does Mop do with the cap?**

● runs with it

○ eats it

○ hides it

13 **What bad thing happens to Mop?**

○ She gets lost.

● She gets stuck.

○ She gets a cap.

14 **What happens at the end of the story?**

● Dan helps Mop.

○ Mop runs away.

○ Mop gets a snack.

15 **Why did the author write the story?**

○ to explain something

○ to get people to do something

● to tell a funny story

GO ON

Common Core State Standards

Questions 11–14: CCSS Informational Text 1. Ask and answer questions about key details in a text.
Question 15: CCSS Informational Text 8. Identify the reasons an author gives to support points in a text.

Name _____

WRITTEN RESPONSE TO THE SELECTION

Look Back and Write Look back at pages 90 and 91. Write about the job of one of the people you see.

Use the list in the box below to help you as you write.

REMEMBER—YOU SHOULD

☐   tell about the job of a person in the selection.

☐   use examples from the selection in your answer.

☐   try to use correct spelling, capitalization, punctuation, grammar, and sentences.

GO ON

Common Core State Standards

CCSS Writing 2. Write informative/explanatory texts in which they name a topic, supply some facts about the topic, and provide some sense of closure. (Also **CCSS Writing 8., CCSS Language 1., CCSS Language 2.**)

Weekly Test 9 Unit 2 Week 3

Name _____

HIGH-FREQUENCY WORDS

Directions
Fill in the circle next to the word that fills the blank.

1 He ran _____ the hill.

- ○ put
- ● down
- ○ stop

2 The dog went _____.

- ● inside
- ○ that
- ○ take

3 I will go to the park _____.

- ○ could
- ○ they
- ● now

4 She put her watch _____.

- ● there
- ○ need
- ○ them

5 They play games _____.

- ○ want
- ● together
- ○ come

Common Core State Standards

Questions 1–5: CCSS Foundational Skills 3.g. Recognize and read grade-appropriate irregularly spelled words.

PHONICS

Directions
Fill in the circle next to the word that fills the blank.

6 She told a <u>joke</u>.

Which word has the same sound as the <u>o</u> in <u>joke</u>?

- ○ come
- ○ good
- ● rode

7 I want to go <u>home</u>.

Which word has the same sound as the <u>o</u> in <u>home</u>?

- ○ into
- ● those
- ○ could

Directions
Fill in the circle next to the word that fills the blank.

8 _____ be home later.

- ● I'll
- ○ 'Ill
- ○ Il'1

9 He _____ going to meet us there.

- ○ is'nt
- ○ isnt'
- ● isn't

10 _____ happy in school.

- ○ Im'
- ● I'm
- ○ Im

GO ON

> **Common Core State Standards**

Questions 6–7: CCSS Foundational Skills 3. Know and apply grade-level phonics and word analysis skills in decoding words.
Questions 8–10: CCSS Language 2.d. Use conventional spelling for words with common spelling patterns and for frequently occurring irregular words.

Name _____

COMPREHENSION

Pet Mice

Jane likes mice. Mice make her smile.

Jane gets five white mice as pets. She makes a safe cage for them.

Jane puts the mice in the cage. The mice sit. Then the mice run.

Jane puts nuts in a dish. She puts the dish in the cage.

The mice eat. Then the mice make nests and get in.

At last they rest. What nice mice!

GO ON

Directions

Fill in the circle next to the answer.

11 **What is the first thing Jane does after she gets the mice?**

- ○ She feeds the mice nuts.
- ○ She cleans their dish.
- ● She makes a safe cage.

12 **What does Jane do next?**

- ● She puts the mice in the cage.
- ○ She puts nuts in a dish.
- ○ She likes mice best.

13 **What do the mice do after they sit?**

- ○ They sleep.
- ● They run.
- ○ They eat.

14 **What happens after the mice eat?**

- ○ They get some rest.
- ○ They run.
- ● They make nests.

15 **What is the last thing the mice do?**

- ○ They get in their nests.
- ● They rest.
- ○ They like nuts.

GO ON

Common Core State Standards

Questions 11–15: **CCSS Literature 3.** Describe characters, settings, and major events in a story, using key details.

Name _____

WRITTEN RESPONSE TO THE SELECTION

> **Look Back and Write** Look back at page 125. Write about how this animal community helped each other. Give evidence from the story to support your answer.

Use the list in the box below to help you as you write.

REMEMBER—YOU SHOULD

- ☐ tell how the animals helped each other.

- ☐ use examples from the story in your answer.

- ☐ try to use correct spelling, capitalization, punctuation, grammar, and sentences.

Common Core State Standards

CCSS Writing 2. Write informative/explanatory texts in which they name a topic, supply some facts about the topic, and provide some sense of closure. (Also **CCSS Writing 8., CCSS Language 1., CCSS Language 2.**)

Weekly Test 10 Unit 2 Week 4

Name _____

HIGH-FREQUENCY WORDS

Directions
Fill in the circle next to the word that fills the blank.

1 **She walked _____ the park.**

○ many

○ has

● around

2 **Did you _____ your homework?**

○ we

● find

○ this

3 **The dog ate all the _____ .**

● food

○ grow

○ could

4 **May I have a glass of _____?**

○ who

● water

○ for

5 **The ball is _____ the bed.**

○ want

○ good

● under

Common Core State Standards

Questions 1–5: CCSS Foundational Skills 3.g. Recognize and read grade-appropriate irregularly spelled words.

PHONICS

Directions
Fill in the circle next to the answer.

6 The dog is <u>huge</u>.

Which word has the same sound as the <u>u</u> in <u>huge</u>?

- ○ home
- ● tube
- ○ under

7 <u>These</u> flowers are pretty.

Which name has the same sound as the first <u>e</u> in <u>these</u>?

- ● Pete
- ○ Mike
- ○ Ben

Directions
Fill in the circle next to the word that should replace the underlined word.

8 He <u>want</u> a new toy.

- ○ went
- ○ wantid
- ● wanted

9 Kelly <u>walk</u> to the store.

- ○ walkdid
- ● walked
- ○ walkd

10 She <u>work</u> at the mall.

- ● worked
- ○ workd
- ○ workdid

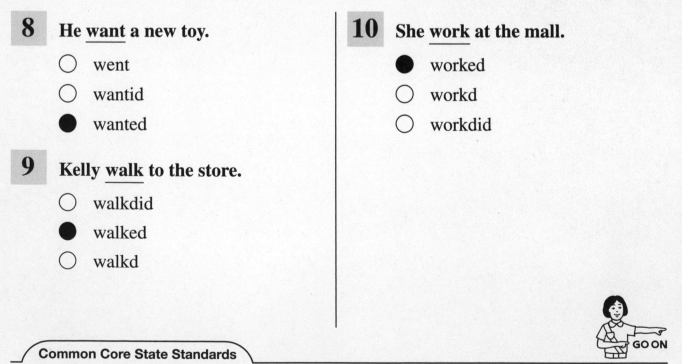

GO ON

Common Core State Standards

Questions 6–7: CCSS Foundational Skills 3. Know and apply grade-level phonics and word analysis skills in decoding words.
Questions 8–10: CCSS Language 2.d. Use conventional spelling for words with common spelling patterns and for frequently occurring irregular words.

Name _____

COMPREHENSION

What Duck Is This?

All ducks are birds that swim.

Ducks kick in the water to swim.

This small duck swims and kicks in the water.

Like all ducks, this duck quacks.

The wings of this duck are black and tan.

The bill of this duck is yellow.

The top of this duck is green.

The neck of this duck is white.

What duck is this?

GO ON

Directions
Fill in the circle next to the answer.

11 **What is the passage about?**
- ○ swimming
- ○ animals
- ● ducks

12 **How do ducks swim?**
- ● kicking their feet in the water
- ○ splashing in the water
- ○ diving deep into the water

13 **What color are the wings of this duck?**
- ● black and tan
- ○ yellow and green
- ○ white

14 **What color neck does this duck have?**
- ○ yellow
- ○ tan
- ● white

15 **Why did the author write this passage?**
- ○ to explain how to do something
- ● to describe something
- ○ to tell a story about something

GO ON

1 Copyright © Pearson Education, Inc., or its affiliates. All Rights Reserved.

> **Common Core State Standards**

Questions 11–14: **CCSS Informational Text 2.** Identify the main topic and retell key details of a text.
Question 15: **CCSS Informational Text 8.** Identify the reasons an author gives to support points in a text.

Name _____

WRITTEN RESPONSE TO THE SELECTION

Look Back and Write Look back at pages 158 and 159. Write about one animal that lives in the forest. Use evidence from the selection to support your answer.

Use the list in the box below to help you as you write.

REMEMBER—YOU SHOULD

☐ tell about an animal that lives in the forest.

☐ use examples from the story in your answer.

☐ try to use correct spelling, capitalization, punctuation, grammar, and sentences.

GO ON

Common Core State Standards

CCSS Writing 2. Write informative/explanatory texts in which they name a topic, supply some facts about the topic, and provide some sense of closure. (Also **CCSS Writing 8., CCSS Language 1., CCSS Language 2.**)

Weekly Test 11 Unit 2 Week 5

Name _____

HIGH-FREQUENCY WORDS

Directions
Fill in the circle next to the word that fills the blank.

1 She _____ has a cat.
- ● also
- ○ time
- ○ new

2 There are four people in my _____ .
- ○ want
- ○ see
- ● family

3 The _____ truck is blue.
- ○ and
- ● other
- ○ now

4 _____ dogs are big.
- ● Some
- ○ Use
- ○ They

5 They like _____ little cat.
- ○ around
- ● their
- ○ but

Common Core State Standards

Questions 1–5: CCSS Foundational Skills 3.g. Recognize and read grade-appropriate irregularly spelled words.

GO ON

Weekly Test 12 Unit 2 Week 6

103

PHONICS

Directions
Fill in the circle next to the answer.

6 I don't want to <u>be</u> late.

Which word has the same sound as the <u>e</u> in <u>be</u>?

○ their
○ use
● we

7 The <u>tree</u> is tall.

Which word has the same sound as the <u>ee</u> in <u>tree</u>?

○ new
● feet
○ some

Directions
Choose the correct way to divide the underlined word into syllables. Fill in the circle next to your answer.

8 We saw <u>hippos</u> at the zoo.

● hip / pos
○ hipp / os
○ hippo / s

9 An <u>insect</u> has six legs.

○ ins / ect
● in / sect
○ i / nsect

10 The dress is made of <u>velvet</u>.

○ ve / lvet
○ velve / t
● vel / vet

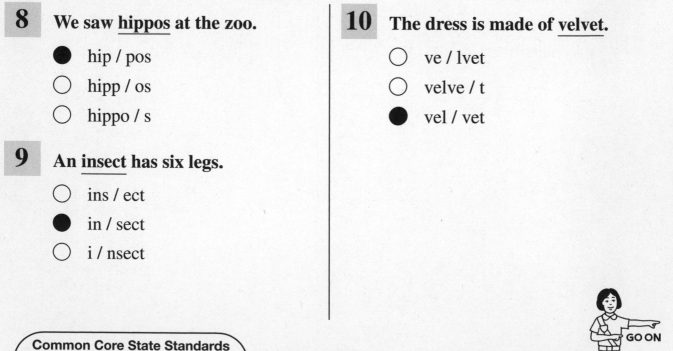
GO ON

> **Common Core State Standards**

Questions 6–7: CCSS Foundational Skills 3. Know and apply grade-level phonics and word analysis skills in decoding words.
Questions 8–10: CCSS Foundational Skills 3.d. Use knowledge that every syllable must have a vowel sound to determine the number of syllables in a printed word.

Name _____

COMPREHENSION

Cats and Rabbits

Are cats and rabbits the same?

Cats and rabbits can be the same size. Cats and rabbits jump.

Cats can be tan, black, and white. Rabbits can be tan, black, and white.

Kids like to pet cats and rabbits. Kids like to run and hop with them.

Cats and rabbits make good pets.

Are cats and rabbits not the same?

Cats like to chase rabbits. Rabbits don't chase cats.

Look out, rabbits! Run fast!

GO ON

Directions

Fill in the circle next to the answer.

11 Why did the author write this passage?

- ○ to tell a story about cats and rabbits
- ● to tell how cats and rabbits are alike and different
- ○ to tell how to take care of cats and rabbits

12 What colors can both cats and rabbits be?

- ● tan, black, and white
- ○ red, orange, and pink
- ○ green, blue, and purple

13 What are two reasons kids like both cats and rabbits?

- ○ Kids like to feed and care for them.
- ○ Kids like to put them into cages.
- ● Kids like to pet and play with them.

14 As pets, how are cats and rabbits the same?

- ● They both make good pets.
- ○ They both are big pets.
- ○ They both make bad pets.

15 What is one big difference between cats and rabbits?

- ○ Cats and rabbits are different sizes.
- ● Cats chase rabbits, but rabbits don't chase cats.
- ○ Cats jump, but rabbits don't jump.

GO ON

/ **Common Core State Standards** \

Question 11: CCSS Informational Text 8. Identify the reasons an author gives to support points in a text.
Questions 12–15: CCSS Informational Text 3. Describe the connection between two individuals, events, ideas, or pieces of information in a text.

Name _____

WRITTEN RESPONSE TO THE SELECTION

Look Back and Write Look back at page 183. What is the queen bee's job? Use evidence from the selection to support your answer.

Use the list in the box below to help you as you write.

REMEMBER—YOU SHOULD

☐   explain what the job of a queen bee is.

☐   put your sentences in an order that makes sense.

☐   try to use correct spelling, capitalization, punctuation, grammar, and sentences.

Common Core State Standards

CCSS Writing 2. Write informative/explanatory texts in which they name a topic, supply some facts about the topic, and provide some sense of closure. (Also **CCSS Writing 8.**, **CCSS Language 1.**, **CCSS Language 2.**)

Name _____

HIGH-FREQUENCY WORDS

Directions
Fill in the circle next to the word that fills the blank.

1 We _____ sit here.

○ am
● always
○ things

2 He will sleep all _____.

● day
○ become
○ to

3 There is _____ in the box.

● nothing
○ family
○ new

4 The cat _____ in the yard.

○ of
● stays
○ now

5 We do _____ together.

○ when
○ they
● everything

GO ON

Common Core State Standards

Questions 1–5: CCSS Foundational Skills 3.g. Recognize and read grade-appropriate irregularly spelled words.

PHONICS

Directions
Fill in the circle next to the answer.

6 This is <u>my</u> cat.

Which word has the same ending sound as the <u>y</u> in <u>my</u>?

● by

○ bunny

○ me

7 Read us a <u>story</u>.

Which word has the same ending sound as the <u>y</u> in <u>story</u>?

○ fly

● sorry

○ lie

8 Let's say <u>hi</u> to Sam.

Which word has the same sound as the <u>i</u> in <u>hi</u>?

○ lay

○ she

● tie

9 <u>We</u> liked the cake.

Which word has the same sound as the <u>e</u> in <u>We</u>?

○ wet

○ way

● be

10 It is time to <u>go</u>.

Which word has the same sound as the <u>o</u> in <u>go</u>?

● so

○ moon

○ say

GO ON

Common Core State Standards

Questions 6–10: CCSS Language 2.e. Spell untaught words phonetically, drawing on phonemic awareness and spelling conventions.

Name _____

COMPREHENSION

A Duck Makes a Nest

In the spring, a duck will make a nest.

The duck picks a good spot for the nest. She will not make the nest

by the water. The water is not safe for the baby ducks.

The duck looks for some sticks. It also looks for twigs and grass.

She uses them to make the nest.

Then she lays her eggs. The nest will be the home for the baby

ducks for many days. The nest will keep the baby ducks warm.

Then the eggs hatch. The baby ducks come out. They stay by their mom.

When it is time to go, the little ducks can fly.

GO ON

Directions

Fill in the circle next to the answer.

11 **When does a duck make a nest?**

    ○   in the summer

    ○   in the fall

    ●   in the spring

12 **What does the duck do first to build a nest?**

    ○   She lays the eggs.

    ●   She picks a good spot.

    ○   She looks for sticks.

13 **When does a duck look for twigs and grass?**

    ●   before it builds the nest

    ○   as soon as the baby ducks can fly

    ○   after it lays the eggs

14 **What happens after the eggs hatch?**

    ●   The baby ducks stay by their mom.

    ○   The baby ducks go in the water.

    ○   The mother duck looks for sticks.

15 **What happens last?**

    ○   The eggs hatch.

    ●   The baby ducks fly away.

    ○   The baby ducks swim in the water.

Common Core State Standards

Questions 11–15: CCSS Literature 3. Describe characters, settings, and major events in a story, using key details.

Name _____

WRITTEN RESPONSE TO THE SELECTION

Look Back and Write Look back at page 23. Why is a sunny spot good for growing plants? Write about it.

Use the list in the box below to help you as you write.

REMEMBER—YOU SHOULD

☐   write about why a sunny spot is good for growing plants.

☐   think about what you know about plants and use these facts in your answer.

☐   try to use correct spelling, capitalization, punctuation, grammar, and sentences.

⎛ **Common Core State Standards** ⎞

CCSS Writing 2. Write informative/explanatory texts in which they name a topic, supply some facts about the topic, and provide some sense of closure. (Also **CCSS Writing 8.**, **CCSS Language 1.**, **CCSS Language 2.**)

Name _____

HIGH-FREQUENCY WORDS

Directions
Fill in the circle next to the word that fills the blank.

1 Do you have _____ pets?

- ○ from
- ○ hat
- ● any

2 Did your dog have _____ water?

- ○ way
- ● enough
- ○ sure

3 Is she _____ at home?

- ● ever
- ○ were
- ○ park

4 _____ frog was green.

- ○ Out
- ○ For
- ● Every

5 Bob has his _____ truck.

- ● own
- ○ then
- ○ some

GO ON

Common Core State Standards

Questions 1–5: CCSS Foundational Skills 3.g. Recognize and read grade-appropriate irregularly spelled words.

PHONICS

Directions
Fill in the circle next to the answer.

6 He works at the <u>bank</u>.

Which word has the same ending sound as the <u>nk</u> in <u>bank</u>?

- ● sink
- ○ pack
- ○ tan

7 This is a gold <u>ring</u>.

Which word has the same ending sound as the <u>ng</u> in <u>ring</u>?

- ○ green
- ● hang
- ○ big

Directions
Fill in the circle next to the compound word that fills the blank.

8 Go _____ to play.
- ○ there
- ● outside
- ○ away

9 She is in the _____.
- ● bedroom
- ○ hall
- ○ class

10 I saw a _____.
- ○ rabbit
- ● housefly
- ○ tree

GO ON

Common Core State Standards

Questions 6–7: CCSS Language 2.d. Use conventional spelling for words with common spelling patterns and for frequently occurring irregular words. Questions 8–10: CCSS Foundational Skills 3.e. Decode two-syllable words following basic patterns by breaking the words into syllables.

Name _____

COMPREHENSION

Gus and Tom

Gus is a pink pig. Gus lives in a big, red home. Gus has a nice place to live. But Gus is sad. "I have no pals," said Gus.

It is wet outside. Gus sees a cat. The cat is wet. "Help!" said the cat.

Gus looks at the cat. The cat looks at Gus. "Hi!" said the cat. "My name is Tom. May I come in? Your home is nice and dry."

"Yes!" said Gus. "But I have no pals. Will you be my pal?"

"I will be your pal!" said Tom. "I like you!"

Gus and Tom play together. Gus plays in the mud. Tom catches mice. Gus and Tom are pals.

GO ON

Directions

Fill in the circle next to the answer.

11 **How are Gus and Tom alike?**

- ○ They are both wet.
- ○ They are both hot.
- ● They both like to play.

12 **How is outside different from the home?**

- ● It is wet.
- ○ It is dry.
- ○ It is red.

13 **Gus and Tom both like to**

- ○ play in the mud.
- ● live in the home.
- ○ catch mice.

14 **How are Gus and Tom different?**

- ● Only one of them is a pig.
- ○ Only one of them wants to be pals.
- ○ Only one of them likes the home.

15 **What makes Tom different from Gus?**

- ○ Tom likes to play in the mud.
- ○ Tom likes to be wet.
- ● Tom likes to catch mice.

GO ON

Common Core State Standards

Questions 11–15: CCSS Literature 9. Compare and contrast the adventures and experiences of characters in stories.

Name _____

WRITTEN RESPONSE TO THE SELECTION

Look Back and Write Look back at page 65. How does Ruby change as she gets bigger? Write about it.

Use the list in the box below to help you as you write.

REMEMBER—YOU SHOULD

☐   tell how Ruby changes as she grows bigger.

☐   use words that describe how Ruby looks and what she does.

☐   try to use correct spelling, capitalization, punctuation, grammar, and sentences.

GO ON

Common Core State Standards

CCSS Literature 3. Describe characters, settings, and major events in a story, using key details. (Also **CCSS Literature 7.**, **CCSS Writing 8.**, **CCSS Language 1.**, **CCSS Language 2.**)

Name _____

HIGH-FREQUENCY WORDS

Directions
Fill in the circle next to the word that fills the blank.

1 The cat has run _____.
- ● away
- ○ can
- ○ got

2 He has a red _____.
- ○ help
- ○ fun
- ● car

3 She plays with her _____ in the park.
- ● friends
- ○ school
- ○ very

4 My _____ is green.
- ○ play
- ○ jump
- ● house

5 We ate _____ dinner.
- ○ fix
- ● our
- ○ use

GO ON

Common Core State Standards

Questions 1–5: CCSS Foundational Skills 3.g. Recognize and read grade-appropriate irregularly spelled words.

PHONICS

Directions
Fill in the circle next to the answer.

6 She works at the <u>store</u>.

Which word has the same sound as the <u>or</u> in <u>store</u>?

● more
○ far
○ tower

7 The present is <u>for</u> you.

Which word has the same sound as the <u>or</u> in <u>for</u>?

○ rot
● worn
○ car

Directions
Fill in the circle next to the word that fills the blank.

8 We wash the _____ after dinner.

○ dishies
○ dishs
● dishes

9 My dog loves to give _____.

● kisses
○ kissies
○ kisss

10 Hal _____ the sink.

○ fixies
○ fixs
● fixes

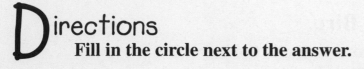

GO ON

Common Core State Standards

Questions 6–7: CCSS Foundational Skills 2.d. Segment spoken single-syllable words into their complete sequence of individual sounds (phonemes). **Questions 8–10: CCSS Foundational Skills 3.f.** Read words with inflectional endings.

Name _____

COMPREHENSION

Birds

This is the park. The park is a nice place. There are many birds in the park.

Some birds are small. The duck is a small bird. Ducks live by the lake. The ducks are beautiful.

Some birds are big. The crane is a big, white bird. Some people think the crane brings good luck.

Some birds are blue. The blue jay is blue. The blue jay likes to hide in trees.

All birds have wings. Many can fly. Some can not fly.

GO ON

Directions

Fill in the circle next to the answer.

11 **Which statement can you prove?**

○ The park is a nice place.

● The crane is a big, white bird.

○ The ducks are beautiful.

12 **Which statement is a fact?**

● Some birds are small.

○ Some people think the crane brings good luck.

○ The park is a nice place.

13 **Which is true of all birds?**

○ All birds hide in trees.

○ All birds are blue.

● All birds have wings.

14 **Which statement is an opinion?**

○ The duck is a small bird.

○ Ducks live by the lake.

● The ducks are beautiful.

15 **It is a fact that**

● some birds cannot fly.

○ the crane brings good luck.

○ the park is nice.

GO ON

1 Copyright © Pearson Education, Inc., or its affiliates. All Rights Reserved.

Common Core State Standards

Questions 11–15: CCSS Informational Text 3. Describe the connection between two individuals, events, ideas, or pieces of information in a text.

Name _____

WRITTEN RESPONSE TO THE SELECTION

Look Back and Write Look back at page 100. Why do you think the mother mouse keeps the baby mice in the nest? Write about it.

Use the list in the box below to help you as you write.

REMEMBER—YOU SHOULD

☐ explain why the mother mouse keeps the baby mice in the nest.

☐ use facts from the story in your answer.

☐ try to use correct spelling, capitalization, punctuation, grammar, and sentences.

Common Core State Standards

CCSS Writing 2. Write informative/explanatory texts in which they name a topic, supply some facts about the topic, and provide some sense of closure. (Also **CCSS Writing 8., CCSS Language 1., CCSS Language 2.**)

Name _____

HIGH-FREQUENCY WORDS

Directions
Fill in the circle next to the word that fills the blank.

1 He is _____ of the dark.

○ grow
○ could
● afraid

2 She forgot her lunch _____.

○ family
● again
○ live

3 There are only a _____ cookies left.

● few
○ blue
○ many

4 I know _____ to tie my shoes.

● how
○ soon
○ there

5 I want to _____ a book.

○ play
● read
○ come

GO ON

Common Core State Standards

Questions 1–5: CCSS Foundational Skills 3.g. Recognize and read grade-appropriate irregularly spelled words.

Weekly Test 16 Unit 3 Week 4

127

PHONICS

Directions
Fill in the circle next to the answer.

6 Hummingbirds like <u>nectar</u>.

Which word has the same sound as the <u>ar</u> in <u>nectar</u>?

- ○ snore
- ● dollar
- ○ play

7 The <u>farmer</u> works hard.

Which word has the same sound as the <u>ar</u> in <u>farmer</u>?

- ● art
- ○ more
- ○ bear

Directions
Choose the correct ending for the underlined word. Fill in the circle next to the answer.

8 She <u>plan</u> to go out with her family.

- ● planned
- ○ planedd
- ○ planed

9 She <u>step</u> on my foot!

- ○ steped
- ○ stepedd
- ● stepped

10 My father is <u>call</u> from far away.

- ○ callen
- ● calling
- ○ caling

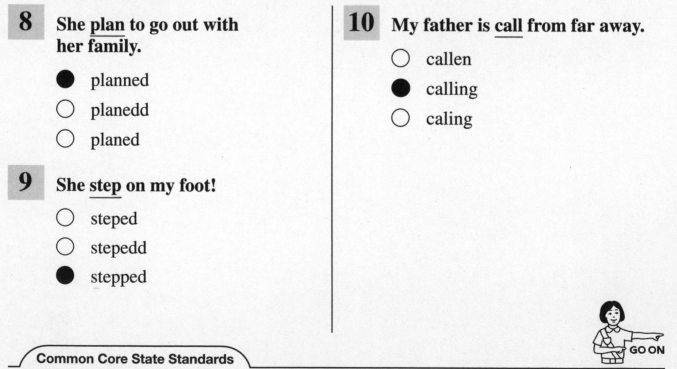

GO ON

> **Common Core State Standards**

Questions 6–7: CCSS Language 2.d. Use conventional spelling for words with common spelling patterns and for frequently occurring irregular words. **Questions 8–10: CCSS Foundational Skills 3.f.** Read words with inflectional endings.

Name _____

COMPREHENSION

How to Take Care of a Plant

When you get a plant, make sure you are good to it. Your plant needs help to grow.

Put the plant in a spot that has sun. Plants need the sun to live.

Then you have to water the plant. Plants also need water to live. Do not let your plant have too much water. If you do, you can kill it. Make sure the plant is dry when you water it.

Some plants also need food. You can give the plant food when you water it.

Soon your plant will grow and become big. It will be beautiful!

GO ON

Directions

Fill in the circle next to the answer.

11 Why did the writer write this story?

- ● to explain how to take care of a plant
- ○ to tell about the different kinds of plants
- ○ to say that a plant is the best gift to give

12 The writer tells you not to let your plant have too much water because

- ○ watering plants takes too much time.
- ● too much water can kill the plant.
- ○ water is not good for plants.

13 Why did the writer tell you to put your plant in the sun?

- ○ Plants look nice in the sun.
- ● Plants need the sun to live.
- ○ Plants need water to live.

14 Why did the writer say that your plant will soon be beautiful?

- ● to make you want to own a plant
- ○ to tell you what kind of plant to get
- ○ to explain what plants look like

15 The writer tells you to water the plant because

- ○ it needs sun to live.
- ○ it needs food to live.
- ● it needs water to live.

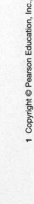

GO ON

Common Core State Standards

Questions 11–15: CCSS Literature 1. Ask and answer questions about key details in a text.

Name _____

WRITTEN RESPONSE TO THE SELECTION

Look Back and Write Look back at page 134. What advice does Frog give to Toad? Write about it.

Use the list in the box below to help you as you write.

REMEMBER—YOU SHOULD

☐   tell what advice Frog gives to Toad.

☐   tell the most important ideas.

☐   try to use correct spelling, capitalization, punctuation, grammar, and sentences.

Common Core State Standards

CCSS Writing 2. Write informative/explanatory texts in which they name a topic, supply some facts about the topic, and provide some sense of closure. (Also **CCSS Writing 8., CCSS Language 1., CCSS Language 2.**)

Name _____

HIGH-FREQUENCY WORDS

Directions
Fill in the circle next to the word that fills the blank.

1 **Are you _____ with your chores?**

- ● done
- ○ play
- ○ around

2 **Do you _____ where she is?**

- ○ look
- ○ go
- ● know

3 **We have to _____ the cart to market.**

- ○ find
- ● push
- ○ put

4 **My mother wants to _____ her old town.**

- ○ take
- ○ grow
- ● visit

5 **_____ until your father comes home.**

- ● Wait
- ○ Paper
- ○ Snap

Common Core State Standards

Questions 1–5: CCSS Foundational Skills 3.g. Recognize and read grade-appropriate irregularly spelled words.

GO ON

PHONICS

Directions
Fill in the circle next to the answer.

6 Mother will be home <u>after</u> work.

Which word has the same sound as the <u>er</u> in <u>after</u>?

○ live
○ torn
● her

7 I saw a <u>bird</u>.

Which word has the same sound as the <u>ir</u> in <u>bird</u>?

● first
○ tear
○ pour

8 He <u>hurt</u> his leg.

Which word has the same sound as the <u>ur</u> in <u>hurt</u>?

○ tar
● fur
○ more

Directions
Fill in the circle next to the word that fills the blank.

9 _____ going to buy a new car?

● Who's
○ Who'se
○ Whos

10 _____ seen each other at school.

● We've
○ Weve
○ Wev'e

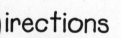

> **Common Core State Standards**
>
> Questions 6–10: CCSS Foundational Skills 3. Know and apply grade-level phonics and word analysis skills in decoding words.

Name _____

COMPREHENSION

Animals Are Always Around!

Zebras and hippos live in hot places. Hippos like the water.

Zebras are cute. Zebras look like little horses. They have black and white stripes.

Squirrels live in the park or the forest. Squirrels have fur. Many squirrels seem to like people. Squirrels like nuts.

Bears live in the forest. Bears are big. Many bears have black or brown fur.

Some bears have white fur. They are called polar bears. Polar bears live in cold places. They are beautiful bears.

Cats can be inside or out. Cats are sweet. They like to play.

GO ON

Directions

Fill in the circle next to the answer.

11 Which statement can you prove?

- ○ Zebras are cute.
- ● Zebras live in hot places.
- ○ Cats are sweet.

12 You cannot prove that zebras

- ○ look like little horses.
- ● are cute.
- ○ have black and white stripes.

13 One fact about cats is that they

- ● like to play.
- ○ are sweet.
- ○ are beautiful.

14 Which statement is not a fact?

- ○ Polar bears have white fur.
- ○ Polar bears live in cold places.
- ● Polar bears are beautiful.

15 It is a fact that

- ● squirrels have fur.
- ○ polar bears are beautiful.
- ○ cats are sweet.

GO ON

Common Core State Standards

Questions 11–15: CCSS Informational Text 3. Describe the connection between two individuals, events, ideas, or pieces of information in a text.

Name _____

WRITTEN RESPONSE TO THE SELECTION

Look Back and Write Look back at page 170. Why aren't these butterflies afraid of birds? Write about it.

Use the list in the box below to help you as you write.

REMEMBER—YOU SHOULD

☐   tell why the butterflies aren't afraid of birds.

☐   use a fact from the selection in your answer.

☐   try to use correct spelling, capitalization, punctuation, grammar, and sentences.

Common Core State Standards

CCSS Writing 2. Write informative/explanatory texts in which they name a topic, supply some facts about the topic, and provide some sense of closure. (Also **CCSS Informational Text 3., CCSS Writing 5., CCSS Writing 8., CCSS Language 1., Language 2.**)

Weekly Test 17 Unit 3 Week 5

Name _____

HIGH-FREQUENCY WORDS

Directions
Fill in the circle next to the word that fills the blank.

1 I read _____ I go to bed.
- ● before
- ○ back
- ○ from

2 _____ Jo have the ball?
- ○ When
- ○ Be
- ● Does

3 Tim will say _____ to Sam.
- ● good-bye
- ○ did
- ○ very

4 _____ no, I just lost my pen!
- ○ Am
- ● Oh
- ○ Do

5 The dog _____ come in the house.
- ● won't
- ○ no
- ○ bike

GO ON

Common Core State Standards

Questions 1–5: CCSS Foundational Skills 3.g. Recognize and read grade-appropriate irregularly spelled words.

PHONICS

Directions
Fill in the circle next to the answer.

6 I like <u>fudge</u>.

Which word has the same sound as the <u>dge</u> in <u>fudge</u>?

- ○ herd
- ● judge
- ○ gas

7 He stood on the <u>ledge</u>.

Which word has the same sound as the <u>dge</u> in <u>ledge</u>?

- ● dodge
- ○ yellow
- ○ grow

Directions
Fill in the circle next to the word that fills the blank.

8 The tower is the _____ building in town.

- ○ tall
- ● tallest
- ○ taller

9 That music is the _____ I have ever heard.

- ○ loud
- ○ louder
- ● loudest

10 An elephant is _____ than a bear.

- ● bigger
- ○ big
- ○ biggest

GO ON

⌐ **Common Core State Standards** ⌐

Questions 6–7: CCSS Language 2.d. Use conventional spelling for words with common spelling patterns and for frequently occurring irregular words. **Questions 8–10: CCSS Language 4.b.** Use frequently occurring affixes as a clue to the meaning of a word.

Name _____

COMPREHENSION

Friends Come Over

Ben, Sam, and Pam are friends.

Ben and Sam go to see Pam. They call, "Pam!"

Pam comes out. Ben and Sam say, "Hi, Pam!"

Ben gave Pam a small doll. Sam gave Pam some flowers.

Pam says, "Thank you! I like the doll very much. The flowers are beautiful."

Ben and Sam ask Pam, "How old are you on this day?"

Pam says, "I am seven! Come in and have some cake with me!"

GO ON

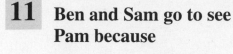 **irections**
Fill in the circle next to the answer.

11 Ben and Sam go to see
Pam because

- ● they are her friends.
- ○ they go to school with her.
- ○ they live in her house.

12 Based on the story, you can
tell that

- ○ Pam does not like Sam
and Ben.
- ● Pam is glad to see Sam
and Ben.
- ○ Pam is afraid of Sam and Ben.

13 Last year Pam was

- ○ four years old.
- ○ five years old.
- ● six years old.

14 You can tell from the story that
today is

- ● Pam's birthday.
- ○ Sam's birthday.
- ○ Ben's birthday.

15 Why do Ben and Sam give Pam
a doll and flowers?

- ○ She is sick today.
- ● Today is her birthday.
- ○ She asked for a doll
and flowers.

GO ON

Common Core State Standards

Questions 11–15: **CCSS Literature 1.** Ask and answer questions about key details in a text.

Name _____

WRITTEN RESPONSE TO THE SELECTION

Look Back and Write Look back at pages 198 and 199.
Where do animals go when the days turn cold? Write
about it.

Use the list in the box below to help you as you write.

REMEMBER—YOU SHOULD

☐   tell where the animals go when the days turn cold.

☐   use facts from the selection in your answer.

☐   try to use correct spelling, capitalization, punctuation, grammar,
and sentences.

Common Core State Standards

CCSS Writing 2. Write informative/explanatory texts in which they name a topic, supply some facts about the topic, and provide some
sense of closure. (Also **CCSS Writing 8., CCSS Language 1., CCSS Language 2.**)

Name _____

HIGH-FREQUENCY WORDS

Directions
Fill in the circle next to the word that fills the blank.

1 Jay read _____ a cat.

- ○ and
- ● about
- ○ but

2 _____ you like to go?

- ● Would
- ○ Have
- ○ From

3 Kim will _____ Don a pen.

- ○ jump
- ○ come
- ● give

4 Sam got a big _____.

- ● surprise
- ○ enjoy
- ○ very

5 Mom and Dad always _____.

- ○ for
- ○ where
- ● worry

GO ON

Common Core State Standards

Questions 1–5: CCSS Foundational Skills 3.g. Recognize and read grade-appropriate irregularly spelled words.

PHONICS

Directions
Fill in the circle next to the answer.

6 The <u>train</u> is at the station.

Which word has the same sound as the <u>ai</u> in <u>train</u>?

○ man
● may
○ call

7 It is a good <u>day</u>.

Which word has the same sound as the <u>ay</u> in <u>day</u>?

○ cat
● plain
○ sand

8 I like the sound of <u>rain</u>.

Which word has the same sound as the <u>ai</u> in <u>rain</u>?

● pay
○ land
○ ran

Directions
Fill in the circle next to the word that fills the blank.

9 All of the _____ toys were on the floor.

○ cats
○ cats's
● cats'

10 My _____ room is bigger than mine.

● sister's
○ sisters
○ sister

┌─ **Common Core State Standards** ─

Questions 6–10: CCSS Language 2.d. Use conventional spelling for words with common spelling patterns and for frequently occurring irregular words.

Name _____

COMPREHENSION

The Cat and the Car

Dad was going to work. He stopped at his car. A cat was under it.

"Go away!" Dad yelled. The cat did not go. "A cat is under the car," he told Mom. "What do I do?"

"How about a little food?" Mom said.

Mom put food near the car. The cat saw it. It was a very old cat. "It won't eat," she said to Dad.

"I have to go to work," Dad said to her. "I have to take the car!"

Mom put water by the car. The cat looked at the water.

Mom and Dad saw the cat come out. "Now I can go to work," Dad said.

GO ON

Directions

Fill in the circle next to the answer.

11 **Why can't Dad go to work?**

- ● A cat is under the car.
- ○ Mom's cat is lost.
- ○ His cat is sick.

12 **Why does Dad yell at the cat?**

- ○ He yells at his pets.
- ● He wants it to go.
- ○ He is mean.

13 **Why is Dad upset when he talks to Mom?**

- ○ He cannot find his car.
- ○ Mom is busy.
- ● The cat will not go.

14 **How does Mom try to help the cat?**

- ○ She takes it into the doctor.
- ● She gives it food and water.
- ○ She takes it into the house.

15 **Why does the cat come out?**

- ○ It is lost.
- ● It wants water.
- ○ It wants food.

GO ON

Common Core State Standards

Questions 11–15: CCSS Literature 1. Ask and answer questions about key details in a text.

Name _____

WRITTEN RESPONSE TO THE SELECTION

Look Back and Write Look back at pages 40–43. What is Mama's birthday present from Francisco? Write about it.

Use the list in the box below to help you as you write.

REMEMBER—YOU SHOULD

☐ write about what Francisco gives Mama for her birthday.

☐ use details from the story to describe Mama's present.

☐ try to use correct spelling, capitalization, punctuation, grammar, and sentences.

Common Core State Standards

CCSS Literature 3. Describe characters, settings, and major events in a story, using key details. (Also **CCSS Literature 1.**, **CCSS Literature 7.**, **CCSS Writing 8.**, **CCSS Language 1.**, **CCSS Language 2.**)

Name _____

HIGH-FREQUENCY WORDS

Directions

Fill in the circle next to the word that fills the blank.

1 The _____ are very pretty.
- ○ school
- ○ reading
- ● colors

2 Sue _____ a picture.
- ● drew
- ○ wrote
- ○ hclpcd

3 The bird flew _____ us.
- ○ plcasc
- ● over
- ○ show

4 John made a big _____.
- ● sign
- ○ art
- ○ draw

5 Today is a _____ day.
- ○ vcry
- ○ have
- ● great

Common Core State Standards

Questions 1–5: CCSS Foundational Skills 3.g. Recognize and read grade-appropriate irregularly spelled words.

PHONICS

Directions
Fill in the circle next to the answer.

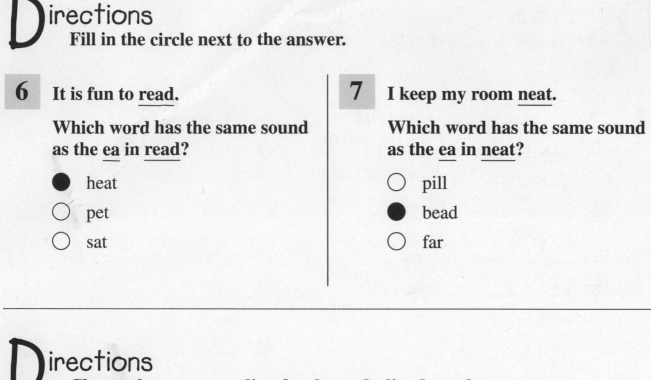

6 It is fun to <u>read</u>.

Which word has the same sound as the <u>ea</u> in read?

- ● heat
- ○ pet
- ○ sat

7 I keep my room <u>neat</u>.

Which word has the same sound as the <u>ea</u> in neat?

- ○ pill
- ● bead
- ○ far

Directions
Choose the correct ending for the underlined word.
Fill in the circle next to the answer.

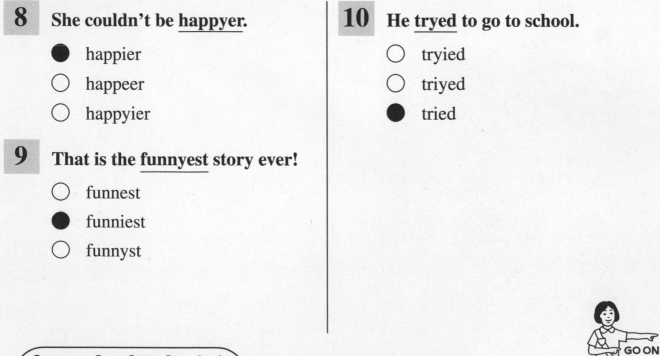

8 She couldn't be <u>happyer</u>.

- ● happier
- ○ happeer
- ○ happyier

9 That is the <u>funnyest</u> story ever!

- ○ funnest
- ● funniest
- ○ funnyst

10 He <u>tryed</u> to go to school.

- ○ tryied
- ○ triyed
- ● tried

GO ON

Common Core State Standards

Questions 6–7: CCSS Foundational Skills 3.c. Know final -e and common vowel team conventions for representing long vowel sounds.
Questions 8–10: CCSS Language 2.d. Use conventional spelling for words with common spelling patterns and for frequently occurring irregular words.

Name _____

HIGH-FREQUENCY WORDS

Directions
Fill in the circle next to the word that fills the blank.

1 The _____ are very pretty.

  ○ school
  ○ reading
  ● colors

2 Sue _____ a picture.

  ● drew
  ○ wrote
  ○ helped

3 The bird flew _____ us.

  ○ please
  ● over
  ○ show

4 John made a big _____.

  ● sign
  ○ art
  ○ draw

5 Today is a _____ day.

  ○ very
  ○ have
  ● great

GO ON

> **Common Core State Standards**

Questions 1–5: CCSS Foundational Skills 3.g. Recognize and read grade-appropriate irregularly spelled words.

PHONICS

Directions
Fill in the circle next to the answer.

6 It is fun to <u>read</u>.

Which word has the same sound
as the <u>ea</u> in <u>read</u>?

- ● heat
- ○ pet
- ○ sat

7 I keep my room <u>neat</u>.

Which word has the same sound
as the <u>ea</u> in <u>neat</u>?

- ○ pill
- ● bead
- ○ far

Directions
Choose the correct ending for the underlined word.
Fill in the circle next to the answer.

8 She couldn't be <u>happyer</u>.

- ● happier
- ○ happeer
- ○ happyier

9 That is the <u>funnyest</u> story ever!

- ○ funnest
- ● funniest
- ○ funnyst

10 He <u>tryed</u> to go to school.

- ○ tryied
- ○ triyed
- ● tried

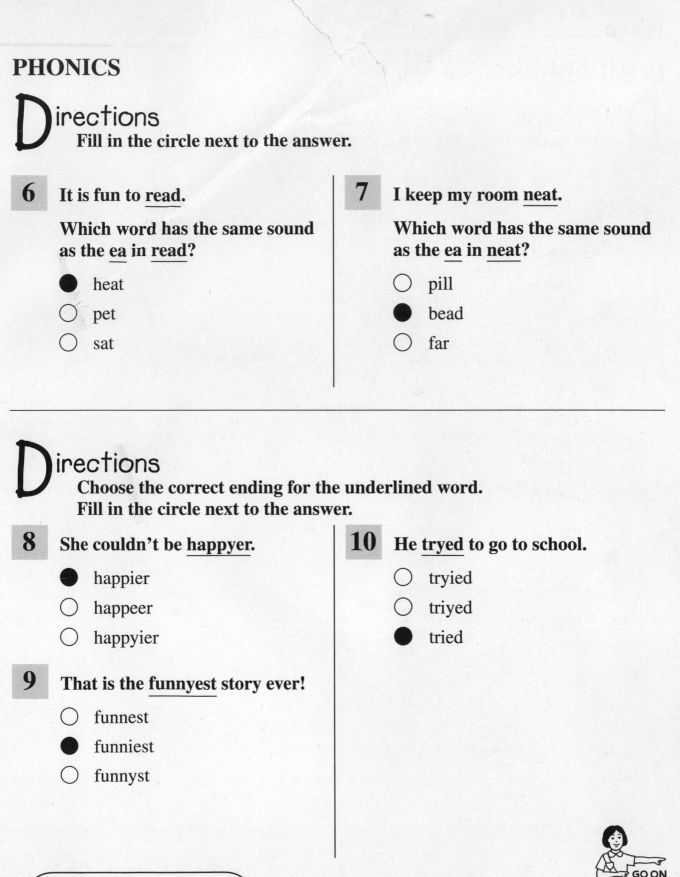

Common Core State Standards

Questions 6–7: CCSS Foundational Skills 3.c. Know final *-e* and common vowel team conventions for representing long vowel sounds.
Questions 8–10: CCSS Language 2.d. Use conventional spelling for words with common spelling patterns and for frequently occurring irregular words.

Name _____

COMPREHENSION

The Bug and the Bird

Tip and Tiff saw a bug under a tree. "Look!" Tiff said. "That bug is very small. It is yellow and green. What a neat bug."

The bug was still. "He is too afraid to get away," Tip said.

Tiff saw a bird in a tree. The bird saw the bug. "We have to help the bug!" she said.

"I know what to do," Tip said. "The bird will not eat him!"

The bird came down from the tree. "Go home!" Tip yelled at him. "There is not food here!" The bird went away.

"That was good!" Tiff said. "The bug is safe!"

GO ON

Directions

Fill in the circle next to the answer.

11 What makes Tip think the bug is afraid?

- ○ The bug sees the bird.
- ● The bug does not move.
- ○ The bug is under a tree.

12 Why is Tiff upset when she sees the bird?

- ● She thinks the bird will eat the bug.
- ○ She thinks the bird is lost.
- ○ She thinks the bird is alone.

13 What does Tip do in the story?

- ● He helps the bug.
- ○ He takes the bug home.
- ○ He helps the bird.

14 This story teaches you to

- ● help people or animals.
- ○ feed bugs and birds in the park.
- ○ look for bugs under trees.

15 Why does Tiff say, "That was good"?

- ○ She is happy that they helped the bird.
- ● She is happy that they helped the bug.
- ○ She is happy that the bird ate the bug.

GO ON

Common Core State Standards

Questions 11–15: CCSS Literature 3. Describe characters, settings, and major events in a story, using key details.

Name _____

WRITTEN RESPONSE TO THE SELECTION

Look Back and Write Look back at page 68. Why is Cinderella sad? Write about it.

Use the list in the box below to help you as you write.

REMEMBER—YOU SHOULD

☐   explain why Cindy is sad in the story.

☐   tell at least two reasons for Cindy's sadness.

☐   try to use correct spelling, capitalization, punctuation, grammar, and sentences.

Common Core State Standards

CCSS Literature 3. Describe characters, settings, and major events in a story, using key details. (Also **CCSS Literature 1.**, **CCSS Literature 4.**, **CCSS Literature 7.**, **CCSS Writing 8.**, **CCSS Language 1.**, **CCSS Language 2.**)

Name _____

HIGH-FREQUENCY WORDS

Directions
Fill in the circle next to the word that fills the blank.

1 We _____ money in the desk.

- ○ gave
- ● found
- ○ came

2 _____ the sun sets, it gets very dark.

- ○ Oh
- ○ One
- ● Once

3 _____ animals live in the forest.

- ● Wild
- ○ Ever
- ○ Around

4 I put food in my _____.

- ● mouth
- ○ head
- ○ rain

5 He _____ the path to the park.

- ○ move
- ● took
- ○ shouted

GO ON

Common Core State Standards

Questions 1–5: CCSS Foundational Skills 3.g. Recognize and read grade-appropriate irregularly spelled words.

PHONICS

Directions
Fill in the circle next to the answer.

6 I cannot find my <u>coat</u>.

Which word has the same sound as the <u>oa</u> in <u>coat</u>?

- ● row
- ○ out
- ○ plow

7 The plane is flying <u>low</u>.

Which word has the same sound as the <u>ow</u> in <u>low</u>?

- ○ long
- ● road
- ○ moon

8 We won the game by one <u>goal</u>!

Which word has the same sound as the <u>oa</u> in <u>goal</u>?

- ○ now
- ● blow
- ○ cow

9 Roger made a big <u>splash</u> in the lake.

Which word has the same sound as the <u>spl</u> in <u>splash</u>?

- ○ shop
- ● split
- ○ spill

10 Kevin finds <u>three</u> dimes under the couch.

Which word has the same sound as the <u>thr</u> in <u>three</u>?

- ● thread
- ○ Thursday
- ○ thorn

GO ON

Common Core State Standards

Questions 6–10: CCSS Language 2.d. Use conventional spelling for words with common spelling patterns and for frequently occurring irregular words.

Name _____

COMPREHENSION

Animals All Around!

Animals are all around you.

You can see squirrels in a park. They are small. They eat nuts and flowers. Some squirrels put food inside trees. They will eat the food some other time.

You can also see birds at the park. Some birds are big. Some are very small. People like to feed the birds.

You may also see a frog at the park. Most are green. They like water. They live in the pond and look for food.

At a zoo, you can see elephants. Elephants are very big. They like to play in the water.

You can see hippos at a zoo too. They also like water. They like to hide under the water.

Many animals are your friends. Be good to them. Animals play, eat, and go to bed just like you do!

Directions

Fill in the circle next to the answer.

11 **Where do some squirrels hide food?**

- ○ under water
- ○ in a circle
- ● in trees

12 **What do people like to do with birds at the park?**

- ○ sell them
- ● feed them
- ○ catch them

13 **What animal might you see in a pond at the park?**

- ● a frog
- ○ an elephant
- ○ a hippo

14 **Where can you see elephants?**

- ● at a zoo
- ○ in trees
- ○ under the water

15 **What do hippos like to do?**

- ○ hide in the park
- ● hide under water
- ○ hide food in trees

GO ON

Common Core State Standards

Questions 11–15: CCSS Informational Text 2. Identify the main topic and retell key details of a text.

160

Name _____

COMPREHENSION

Animals All Around!

Animals are all around you.

You can see squirrels in a park. They are small. They eat nuts and flowers. Some squirrels put food inside trees. They will eat the food some other time.

You can also see birds at the park. Some birds are big. Some are very small. People like to feed the birds.

You may also see a frog at the park. Most are green. They like water. They live in the pond and look for food.

At a zoo, you can see elephants. Elephants are very big. They like to play in the water.

You can see hippos at a zoo too. They also like water. They like to hide under the water.

Many animals are your friends. Be good to them. Animals play, eat, and go to bed just like you do!

Directions
Fill in the circle next to the answer.

11 **Where do some squirrels hide food?**

- ○ under water
- ○ in a circle
- ● in trees

12 **What do people like to do with birds at the park?**

- ○ sell them
- ● feed them
- ○ catch them

13 **What animal might you see in a pond at the park?**

- ● a frog
- ○ an elephant
- ○ a hippo

14 **Where can you see elephants?**

- ● at a zoo
- ○ in trees
- ○ under the water

15 **What do hippos like to do?**

- ○ hide in the park
- ● hide under water
- ○ hide food in trees

 GO ON

Common Core State Standards

Questions 11–15: CCSS Informational Text 2. Identify the main topic and retell key details of a text.

Name _____

WRITTEN RESPONSE TO THE SELECTION

Look Back and Write Look back at the selection. Write about one thing you can see in Washington, D. C.

Use the list in the box below to help you as you write.

REMEMBER—YOU SHOULD

☐ write about something you can see in Washington, D. C.

☐ tell why someone would want to see it.

☐ try to use correct spelling, capitalization, punctuation, grammar, and sentences.

Common Core State Standards

CCSS Writing 2. Write informative/explanatory texts in which they name a topic, supply some facts about the topic, and provide some sense of closure. (Also **CCSS Informational Text 7., CCSS Language 1., CCSS Language 2.**)

Name _____

HIGH-FREQUENCY WORDS

Directions
Fill in the circle next to the word that fills the blank.

1 The sun is _____ the hill.
- ● above
- ○ also
- ○ jump

2 There are _____ pens on the desk.
- ○ that
- ○ sit
- ● eight

3 The _____ is in the sky.
- ○ want
- ● moon
- ○ from

4 They _____ at the joke.
- ● laugh
- ○ have
- ○ dig

5 Do not _____ the hot pan!
- ○ of
- ● touch
- ○ read

GO ON

Common Core State Standards

Questions 1–5: CCSS Foundational Skills 3.g. Recognize and read grade-appropriate irregularly spelled words.

PHONICS

Directions
Fill in the circle next to the answer.

6 Please turn on the <u>light</u>.

Which word has the same sound as the <u>igh</u> in <u>light</u>?

- ● tie
- ○ ghost
- ○ lip

7 It is bad to tell a <u>lie</u>.

Which word has the same sound as the <u>ie</u> in <u>lie</u>?

- ○ mitt
- ○ lean
- ● night

8 We <u>might</u> go to the park.

Which word has the same sound as the <u>igh</u> in <u>might</u>?

- ○ mill
- ● pie
- ○ sit

Directions
Fill in the circle next to the word that fills the blank.

9 His answers were _____ on the test.

- ○ wrung
- ○ rong
- ● wrong

10 Do you _____ Jim's sister?

- ● know
- ○ now
- ○ no

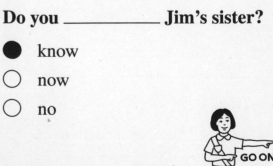
GO ON

⎛ **Common Core State Standards** ⎞

Questions 6–10: CCSS Language 2.d. Use conventional spelling for words with common spelling patterns and for frequently occurring irregular words.

Name _____

COMPREHENSION

Montana

Montana is one of the states. It is a wild and beautiful place. It is also very big!

Montana is home to many animals. There are big animals. There are small animals. Not many people live there. More people live in other states, such as California and New York.

The people who live in Montana work very hard. Some of them are cowboys. Some of them are farmers. Some people work at desks.

In Montana, some people have found very, very old bones of animals. They find them under the ground. People go to Montana to find and study the bones.

Montana is very cold in the winter. It snows a lot there. People who live there must dress warm when it gets cold outside.

In the summer, Montana is warm. Many people go there to watch birds. Some visit to go fishing. Montana is a beautiful place to see.

GO ON

Directions

Fill in the circle next to the answer.

11 **What is Montana?**

- ● a state
- ○ an animal
- ○ a person

12 **Who works in Montana?**

- ○ horses and big bears
- ○ animals that lived long ago
- ● cowboys and farmers

13 **What is under the ground in Montana?**

- ○ snow
- ● animal bones
- ○ birds and fish

14 **In the winter, people in Montana must**

- ○ go fishing.
- ● dress warm.
- ○ farm.

15 **Why do some people visit Montana?**

- ○ to play in the ocean
- ○ to grow corn
- ● to go fishing

GO ON

Common Core State Standards

Questions 11–15: CCSS Informational Text 1. Ask and answer questions about key details in a text.

Name _____

WRITTEN RESPONSE TO THE SELECTION

Look Back and Write Look back at pages 136–137. How do ranch hands keep the herd together? Write about it.

Use the list in the box below to help you as you write.

REMEMBER—YOU SHOULD

- tell how ranch hands keep the herd together.

- use action words to make your writing more interesting.

- try to use correct spelling, capitalization, punctuation, grammar, and sentences.

GO ON

Common Core State Standards

CCSS Writing 2. Write informative/explanatory texts in which they name a topic, supply some facts about the topic, and provide some sense of closure. (Also **CCSS Informational Text 7., CCSS Writing 8., CCSS Language 1., CCSS Language 2.**)

Weekly Test 22 Unit 4 Week 4

Name _____

HIGH-FREQUENCY WORDS

Directions
Fill in the circle next to the word that fills the blank.

1 Liz has a _____ of her mom.

- ○ park
- ● picture
- ○ play

2 My _____ is big.

- ○ run
- ○ take
- ● room

3 Mike _____ in line.

- ○ will
- ● stood
- ○ green

4 I _____ it was going to rain.

- ● thought
- ○ have
- ○ that

5 Did you _____ to take your hat?

- ○ hide
- ○ would
- ● remember

Common Core State Standards

Questions 1–5: CCSS Foundational Skills 3.g. Recognize and read grade-appropriate irregularly spelled words.

GO ON

PHONICS

Directions
Fill in the circle next to the answer.

6 The sky is very <u>blue</u>.

Which word has the same sound as the <u>ue</u> in <u>blue</u>?

- ○ grow
- ○ cut
- ● fruit

7 My coat is <u>new</u>.

Which word has the same sound as the <u>ew</u> in <u>new</u>?

- ● glue
- ○ near
- ○ put

8 My father wears a <u>suit</u> to work.

Which word has the same sound as the <u>ui</u> in <u>suit</u>?

- ○ set
- ● grew
- ○ funny

Directions
Fill in the circle next to the compound word that fills the blank.

9 It is cold _____.

- ● outside
- ○ bedroom
- ○ nowhere

10 Did you pack your _____?

- ○ snowstorm
- ● suitcase
- ○ blackbird

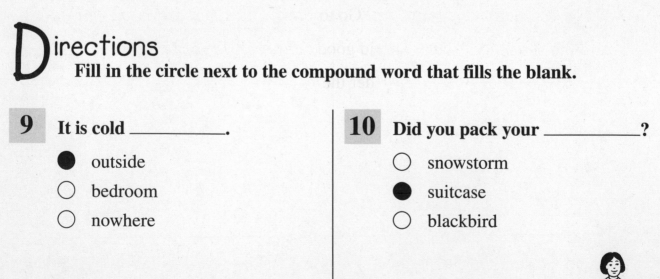

GO ON

Common Core State Standards

Questions 6–10: CCSS Foundational Skills 3. Know and apply grade-level phonics and word analysis skills in decoding words.

Name _____

COMPREHENSION

A New Home

Old Ben was a farmer. Many animals were always around.

One night Old Ben saw a small bear. The bear was cold. Old Ben took the bear into the barn.

The horse was afraid of the bear. Old Ben took the horse to a room away from the bear.

The goose also saw the bear. She had many feathers to keep her warm.

She put down some feathers for the bear. The bear was surprised.

He stared down at the ground. The feathers made a good warm bed.

Old Ben was sure the bear wanted to eat. Inside his house was some honey.

He took the honey. He put some under a tree. "Come over here," he said to the bear. The bear put the honey into his mouth.

Old Ben saw the bear enjoy the food.

Soon Old Ben said to the bear, "Go to bed. This is your new home. We are your new family!" Old Ben said good night to the animals.

He saw the bear go to sleep under the moon.

GO ON

Directions
Fill in the circle next to the answer.

11 This story teaches you to

- ● share what you have with others.
- ○ work with animals on a farm.
- ○ chase bears away from a farm.

12 Old Ben first sees that the bear is

- ○ big and warm.
- ○ tired and hungry.
- ● small and cold.

13 Why does the goose put down feathers for the bear?

- ○ because the farmer tells her to
- ● because she wants to help him
- ○ because the bear is sleepy

14 Why is the bear surprised?

- ○ The horse is afraid of him.
- ● The goose makes a bed for him.
- ○ The farmer gives him honey.

15 Why does Old Ben say, "We are your new family"?

- ● He wants the bear to stay on the farm.
- ○ He wants the bear to leave in the morning.
- ○ He wants the horse to stop being afraid.

 GO ON

Common Core State Standards

Question 11: CCSS Literature 2. Retell stories, including key details, and demonstrate understanding of their central message or lesson.
Questions 12–15: CCSS Literature 3. Describe characters, settings, and major events in a story, using key details.

Name _____

WRITTEN RESPONSE TO THE SELECTION

> **Look Back and Write** Look back at pages 168–169. Why does Peter take his chair to his room? Write about it.

Use the list in the box below to help you as you write.

REMEMBER—YOU SHOULD

 tell why Peter takes his chair to his room.

 use details from the story to explain Peter's actions.

☐ try to use correct spelling, capitalization, punctuation, grammar, and sentences.

Common Core State Standards

CCSS Literature 3. Describe characters, settings, and major events in a story, using key details. (Also **CCSS Literature 1.**, **CCSS Literature 7.**, **CCSS Writing 8.**, **CCSS Language 1.**, **CCSS Language 2.**)

Name _____

HIGH-FREQUENCY WORDS

Directions
Fill in the circle next to the word that fills the blank.

1 Jim _____ his dog to sit.

- ○ opened
- ○ big
- ● told

2 My _____ are red.

- ○ sit
- ● shoes
- ○ have

3 We play ball _____ it is fun.

- ○ before
- ○ come
- ● because

4 Mary can _____ well.

- ○ day
- ● dance
- ○ glass

5 Mark lives _____ the street.

- ● across
- ○ like
- ○ only

GO ON

Common Core State Standards

Questions 1–5: CCSS Foundational Skills 3.g. Recognize and read grade-appropriate irregularly spelled words.

PHONICS

Directions
Fill in the circle next to the answer.

6 The <u>moon</u> is so bright.

Which word has the same sound as the <u>oo</u> in <u>moon</u>?

- ○ sun
- ○ blow
- ● food

7 My <u>room</u> is cold.

Which word has the same sound as the <u>oo</u> in <u>room</u>?

- ● noon
- ○ road
- ○ for

8 They will be here <u>soon</u>.

Which word has the same sound as the <u>oo</u> in <u>soon</u>?

- ○ won
- ○ run
- ● hoop

Directions
Fill in the circle next to the word that fills the blank.

9 The flowers are _____.

- ○ beautifully
- ○ beauty
- ● beautiful

10 He played the music _____.

- ○ sadder
- ● sadly
- ○ sadful

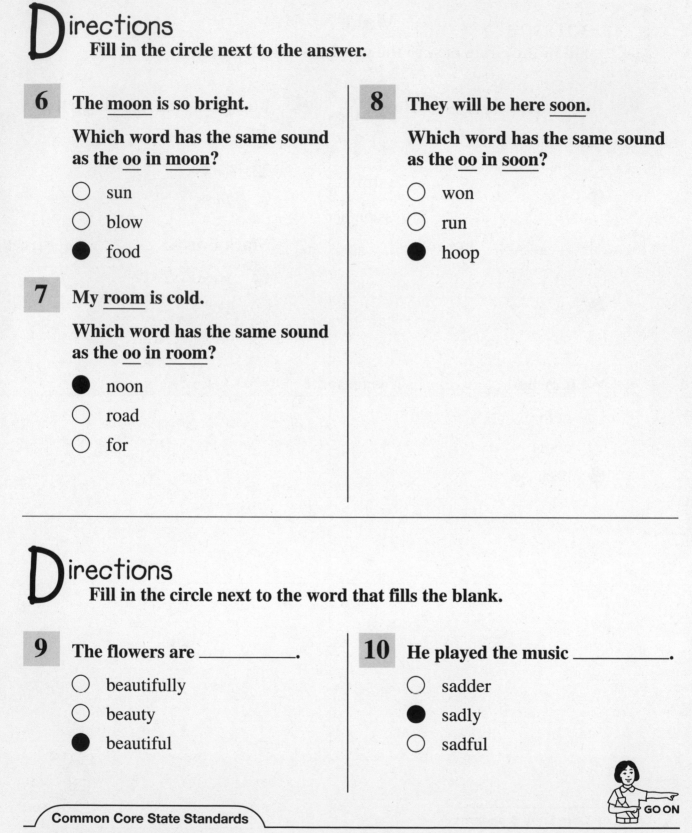

GO ON

Common Core State Standards

Questions 6–10: CCSS Foundational Skills 3. Know and apply grade-level phonics and word analysis skills in decoding words.

Name _____

COMPREHENSION

Meg Makes a Mess

Meg wanted to make a pie. It was a surprise for her mother.

Meg got everything she needed for the pie. She cut up some peaches.

Her mother thought peaches were the best fruit!

Meg got out the eggs. Then she stirred them. The spoon fell from

Meg's hand. Oh, no! It made a mess on her shoes.

Meg turned on the oven. Soon it was warm. Meg put the pie in the oven.

Now it was going to cook.

Meg did not cook the pie for long. She took it out of the oven. It was

a mess.

Her mother was very surprised when she saw the mess that Meg

had made!

GO ON

Directions

Fill in the circle next to the answer.

11 Why does Meg make the pie?

- ● to surprise her mother
- ○ to sell at a bake sale
- ○ to give to her friend Sue

12 Why does Meg use peaches for the pie?

- ○ She has a peach tree outside.
- ○ The peaches were on sale at the store.
- ● It is her mother's favorite fruit.

13 How does Meg make a mess on her shoes?

- ○ An egg fell on them.
- ● The spoon fell on them.
- ○ A peach fell on them.

14 Why is the pie a mess?

- ○ The pie fell on the floor.
- ○ Meg forgot to cook the pie.
- ● Meg did not cook the pie for long.

15 When Meg's mother saw the mess that Meg made, she

- ● was surprised.
- ○ was sad.
- ○ was mad.

GO ON

Common Core State Standards

Questions 11–15: CCSS Literature 3. Describe characters, settings, and major events in a story, using key details.

WRITTEN RESPONSE TO THE SELECTION

Look Back and Write Look back at pages 214–216. What costumes do Henry and Mudge try on? Write about them.

Use the list in the box below to help you as you write.

REMEMBER—YOU SHOULD

 tell about the costumes that Henry and Mudge try on.

 use details about the costumes in your answer.

☐ try to use correct spelling, capitalization, punctuation, grammar, and sentences.

Common Core State Standards

CCSS Literature 3. Describe characters, settings, and major events in a story, using key details. (Also **CCSS Literature 1.,** **CCSS Literature 7., CCSS Writing 8., CCSS Language 1., CCSS Language 2.)**

Name _____

HIGH-FREQUENCY WORDS

Directions
Fill in the circle next to the word that fills the blank.

1 I will go _____ with you.

- ● along
- ○ all
- ○ had

2 Jan stands _____ Nick in the line.

- ○ far
- ○ because
- ● behind

3 Jack has green _____ .

- ● eyes
- ○ eat
- ○ one

4 I am _____ late for school.

- ○ toward
- ○ every
- ● never

5 The baby was _____ my hair.

- ○ store
- ● pulling
- ○ where

GO ON

Common Core State Standards

Questions 1–5: CCSS Foundational Skills 3.g. Recognize and read grade-appropriate irregularly spelled words.

PHONICS

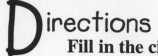irections

Fill in the circle next to the answer.

6 The <u>cows</u> came home after dark.

Which word has the same sound as <u>ow</u> in <u>cows</u>?

○ grow

● flower

○ snow

7 Mike is <u>proud</u> of his new suit.

Which word has the same sound as <u>ou</u> in <u>proud</u>?

○ soup

○ tour

● loud

irections

Fill in the circle next to the answer that shows the correct way to divide the underlined word into syllables.

8 There are three horses in the <u>stable</u>.

● sta / ble

○ stab / le

○ st / able

9 The <u>maple</u> tree is very tall.

○ map / le

○ mapl / e

● ma / ple

10 I have a glass <u>bottle</u> on my desk.

○ bo / ttle

● bot / tle

○ bott / le

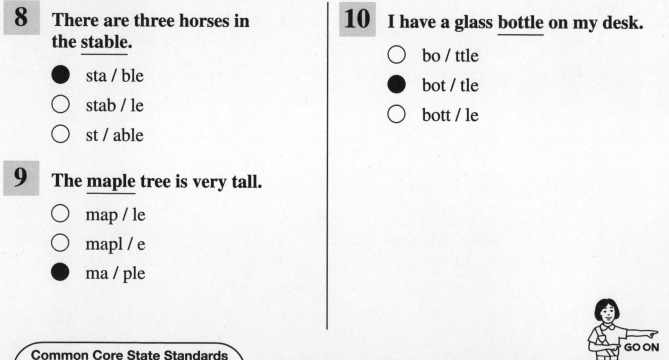

GO ON

> **Common Core State Standards**

Questions 6–7: CCSS Foundational Skills 3. Know and apply grade-level phonics and word analysis skills in decoding words.
Questions 8–10: CCSS Foundational Skills 3.e. Decode two-syllable words following basic patterns by breaking the words into syllables.

Name _____

COMPREHENSION

The Mouse Sisters

Country Mouse and Town Mouse are sisters. Town Mouse tells her sister, "Come and visit me in the town!"

Country Mouse comes to the big town. Town Mouse lives there. She lives in a small blue house. She eats cheese and fruit. She sleeps in a little white bed.

Town Mouse likes her house. Country Mouse likes it too. It not like the big red barn where she lives. She is happy in the town.

Town Mouse is proud to have her sister visit her.

GO ON

Directions

Fill in the circle next to the answer.

11 Town Mouse lives in a

- ○ big red barn.
- ● small blue house.
- ○ little white house.

12 What happens in this story?

- ○ Town Mouse visits Country Mouse.
- ● Country Mouse visits Town Mouse.
- ○ Country Mouse is proud to have her sister visit her.

13 Town Mouse is

- ● proud.
- ○ sad.
- ○ afraid.

14 Where does Town Mouse sleep?

- ○ in the country
- ○ in a big red barn
- ● in a little white bed

15 Where does this story take place?

- ○ on a farm
- ○ in a barn
- ● in the town

Common Core State Standards

Questions 11–15: CCSS Literature 3. Describe characters, settings, and major events in a story, using key details.

Name _____

WRITTEN RESPONSE TO THE SELECTION

Look Back and Write Look back at pages 34–37. Why was Little Chick's idea great? Write about it. Use evidence from the story to support your answer.

Use the list in the box below to help you as you write.

REMEMBER—YOU SHOULD

☐ tell why Little Chick's idea was great.

☐ use examples from the story in your answer.

☐ try to use correct spelling, capitalization, punctuation, grammar, and sentences.

Common Core State Standards

CCSS Literature 3. Describe characters, settings, and major events in a story, using key details. (Also **CCSS Literature 1.**, **CCSS Literature 7.**, **CCSS Writing 8.**, **CCSS Language 1.**, **CCSS Language 2.**)

Name _____

HIGH-FREQUENCY WORDS

Directions

Fill in the circle next to the word that fills the blank.

1 The back _____ is red.
- ○ draw
- ● door
- ○ cold

2 The family _____ the cat.
- ● loved
- ○ swim
- ○ little

3 You _____ read every day.
- ○ what
- ● should
- ○ there

4 _____ comes from a tree.
- ○ Like
- ○ Wait
- ● Wood

5 _____ we see the new movie?
- ● Should
- ○ When
- ○ Going

GO ON

Common Core State Standards

Questions 1–5: CCSS Foundational Skills 3.g. Recognize and read grade-appropriate irregularly spelled words.

PHONICS

Directions
Fill in the circle next to the answer.

6 Kolya <u>found</u> his ball.

Which word has the same sound as <u>ou</u> in <u>found</u>?

- ● shout
- ○ double
- ○ would

7 She can <u>count</u> to ten.

Which word has the same sound as <u>ou</u> in <u>count</u>?

- ○ soul
- ● hound
- ○ court

Directions
Choose the correct way to divide the underlined word into syllables. Fill in the circle next to the answer.

8 The <u>pilot</u> wears a blue hat.

- ○ pil / ot
- ● pi / lot
- ○ pilo / t

9 The <u>baby</u> went to the park with Mom.

- ● ba / by
- ○ b / aby
- ○ bab / y

10 I like the taste of <u>lemons</u>.

- ● lem / ons
- ○ le / mons
- ○ lemo / ns

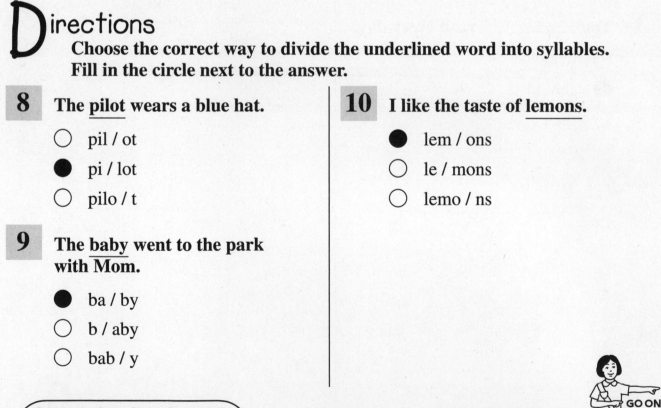

GO ON

Common Core State Standards

Questions 6–7: CCSS Language 2.d. Use conventional spelling for words with common spelling patterns and for frequently occurring irregular words. **Questions 8–10: CCSS Foundational Skills 3.e.** Decode two-syllable words following basic patterns by breaking the words into syllables.

Name _____

Mole and the Baby Bird

COMPREHENSION

A Present for Dad

Sam will make a picture book. It is a present for his father.

First, Sam finds pictures that he likes. He has pictures of his mother and of his family.

Next, Sam finds a small book. He puts each picture in the book. He tapes a picture to each page in the book.

Then Sam draws a picture on the cover. He draws a picture of his father.

Sam shows the book to his mother. She thinks his father will love it.

What does Sam do now? He gives the book to his father!

1 Copyright © Pearson Education, Inc., or its affiliates. All Rights Reserved.

Weekly Test 26   Unit 5 Week 2

189

Directions

Fill in the circle next to the answer.

11 **What is Sam making?**

  ○ a drawing for his sister

  ○ a cake for his mother

  ● a book of pictures for his father

12 **Why is Sam making a picture book?**

  ● to give to his father

  ○ to give to his mother

  ○ to show his friends at school

13 **You can tell that Sam**

  ○ wants to please his mother.

  ● loves his father very much.

  ○ wants to do well in school.

14 **Based on the story, Sam is very good at**

  ○ math.

  ○ sports.

  ● art.

15 **You can tell that Sam's father**

  ○ will be hungry for supper.

  ○ will come home late.

  ● will love the picture book.

GO ON

Common Core State Standards

Questions 11–15: **CCSS Literature 3.** Describe characters, settings, and major events in a story, using key details.

Name _____

WRITTEN RESPONSE TO THE SELECTION

Look Back and Write Look back at page 74. Why does Mole think he's flying? Provide evidence to support your answer.

Use the list in the box below to help you as you write.

REMEMBER—YOU SHOULD

 tell why Mole thinks he is flying.

 use examples from the story in your answer.

☐ try to use correct spelling, capitalization, punctuation, grammar, and sentences.

Common Core State Standards

CCSS Literature 3. Describe characters, settings, and major events in a story, using key details. (Also **CCSS Literature 1.**, **CCSS Literature 7.**, **CCSS Writing 8.**, **CCSS Language 1.**, **CCSS Language 2.**)

Name _____

HIGH-FREQUENCY WORDS

Directions
Fill in the circle next to the word that fills the blank.

1 Harry wants to play
_____ game.

- ● another
- ○ mine
- ○ here

2 _____ of the pens are red.

- ○ Come
- ● None
- ○ Big

3 There are birds _____
the trees.

- ○ have
- ○ hill
- ● among

4 She stayed home _____
of going out.

- ○ from
- ● instead
- ○ when

5 The flowers are growing
_____ the roots of the tree.

- ● among
- ○ after
- ○ slide

GO ON

Common Core State Standards

Questions 1–5: CCSS Foundational Skills 3.g. Recognize and read grade-appropriate irregularly spelled words.

PHONICS

Directions
Fill in the circle next to the answer.

6 "Little Red Riding <u>Hood</u>" is my favorite story.

Which word has the same sound as <u>oo</u> in <u>Hood</u>?

- ○ moon
- ● took
- ○ noon

7 Most pencils are made of <u>wood</u>.

Which word has the same sound as <u>oo</u> in <u>wood</u>?

- ● hook
- ○ boot
- ○ balloon

Directions
Fill in the circle next to the word that fills the blank.

8 The baby _____ at me.

- ● smiled
- ○ smileed
- ○ smilled

9 She _____ out of her uniform.

- ○ changeed
- ● changed
- ○ changd

10 The cat is _____ its eyes.

- ○ closiing
- ○ closeing
- ● closing

Common Core State Standards

Questions 6–7: **CCSS Foundational Skills 3.** Know and apply grade-level phonics and word analysis skills in decoding words.
Questions 8–10: **CCSS Foundational Skills 3.f.** Read words with inflectional endings.

GO ON

Name _____

COMPREHENSION

A Great Animal

Dogs are more than just pets!

Some dogs work on farms. They help other animals that live on the farm stay safe. They stop animals from running away or getting lost.

Some dogs work with detectives. They help to look for clues. They can smell things that people can't. And that helps detectives solve crimes.

One dog even went into space! Her name was Laika. Her job was very important. She showed that living things could be sent into space.

Dogs don't just make great pets. Some dogs also do hard work.

GO ON

Directions

Fill in the circle next to the answer.

11 How are dogs different from other pets?

- ○ They like to be with people.
- ● They help people on the job.
- ○ They are animals.

12 How are detectives and the dogs that work with them alike?

- ● They both look for clues.
- ○ They both work on a farm.
- ○ They can both smell things that people can't.

13 How was Laika different from other dogs?

- ○ She worked with people.
- ● She went into space.
- ○ She helped animals on the farm.

14 How are all the dogs in the story alike?

- ● They all help people with their jobs.
- ○ They all work on farms.
- ○ They all help to solve crimes.

15 How are farm dogs different from dogs that help detectives?

- ● They work with many animals.
- ○ They make great pets.
- ○ They work in space.

GO ON

/ **Common Core State Standards** \

Questions 11–15: CCSS Informational Text 3. Describe the connection between two individuals, events, ideas, or pieces of information in a text.

Name _____

WRITTEN RESPONSE TO THE SELECTION

Look Back and Write Look back at page 108. How do maple seeds move around? Write about it. Use evidence from the story.

Use the list in the box below to help you as you write.

REMEMBER—YOU SHOULD

☐ describe how maple seeds move around.

☐ use details from the selection in your answer.

☐ try to use correct spelling, capitalization, punctuation, grammar, and sentences.

Common Core State Standards

CCSS Informational Text 7. Use the illustrations and details in a text to describe its key ideas. (Also **CCSS Informational Text 1.**, **CCSS Writing 2.**, **CCSS Writing 8.**, **CCSS Language 1.**, **CCSS Language 2.**)

Name _____

HIGH-FREQUENCY WORDS

Directions
Fill in the circle next to the word that fills the blank.

1   Kim _____ to the park.

   ○ before

   ○ have

   ● goes

2   There are many _____ of trees.

   ● kinds

   ○ here

   ○ look

3   The sun is out _____.

   ○ that

   ○ they

   ● today

4   This big box is _____.

   ○ from

   ● heavy

   ○ help

5   Brad sat _____ the wall.

   ● against

   ○ then

   ○ long

GO ON

Common Core State Standards

Questions 1–5: CCSS Foundational Skills 3.g. Recognize and read grade-appropriate irregularly spelled words.

PHONICS

Directions
Fill in the circle next to the answer.

6 Add the eggs as soon as the water **boils**.

Which word has the same sound as **oi** in **boils**?

○ root

● enjoy

○ night

7 A stuffed bear is always a favorite **toy**.

Which word has the same sound as **oy** in **toy**?

● choice

○ soon

○ glow

Directions
Fill in the circle next to the word that fills the blank.

8 The _____ is giving a speech today.

○ govern

○ governed

● governor

9 My _____ says math is fun.

● teacher

○ teaching

○ teach

10 The _____ got on the ship.

○ sail

● sailor

○ sailed

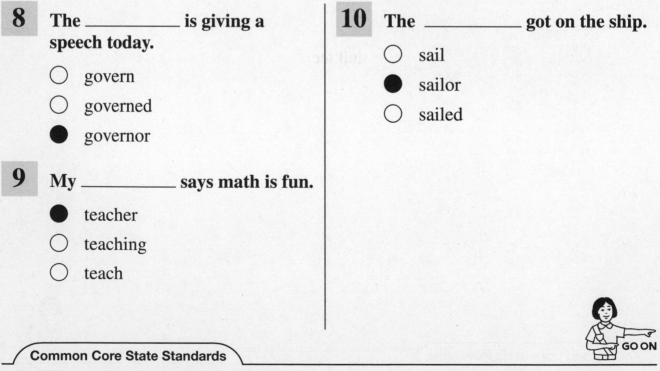

GO ON

1 Copyright © Pearson Education, Inc., or its affiliates. All Rights Reserved.

Common Core State Standards

Questions 6–10: CCSS Foundational Skills 3. Know and apply grade-level phonics and word analysis skills in decoding words.

Name _____

COMPREHENSION

Kittens and Cats

Baby cats are called kittens. The first few weeks in a kitten's life are very important.

When a kitten is born, it cannot see or hear. Its eyes and ears are closed. The kitten's ears start to open when it is about four or five days old.

In the second week, a kitten opens its eyes for the first time. It begins to smell things around it.

When the kitten is three weeks old, it can stand up. It begins to walk about. Its baby teeth begin to show. It can purr.

At five weeks old, kittens start to run and play games. All cats lick their fur to keep it clean. A kitten starts to lick itself at around five weeks.

When the kitten is about eight weeks old, it learns how to hunt. This is how cats in the wild find food. The mother cat teaches her kittens how to hunt.

At twelve weeks, the kitten's adult teeth start to grow in. It can take care of itself now.

GO ON

Directions

Fill in the circle next to the answer.

11 **This story is mostly about**

● how a kitten spends its first few weeks of life.

○ how a cat takes care of her kittens.

○ how nice it is to have a kitten for a pet.

12 **Why does a cat or kitten lick itself?**

○ to play a game

● to keep its fur clean

○ to find food in the wild

13 **How old is a kitten when it starts to play games?**

○ two weeks old

○ three weeks old

● five weeks old

14 **When does the kitten start to get its adult teeth?**

○ at eight weeks

● at twelve weeks

○ at four weeks

15 **When does a kitten start to run?**

○ at two weeks

○ at three weeks

● at five weeks

GO ON

Common Core State Standards

Questions 11–15: CCSS Informational Text 2. Identify the main topic and retell key details of a text.

Name _____

WRITTEN RESPONSE TO THE SELECTION

Look Back and Write Look back at page 148. How would you use an inclined plane to get a big box onto a truck? Provide evidence to support your answer.

Use the list in the box below to help you as you write.

REMEMBER—YOU SHOULD

☐ write how you would load a big box on a truck using an inclined plane.

☐ write the steps in order from beginning to end.

☐ try to use correct spelling, capitalization, punctuation, grammar, and sentences.

GO ON

Common Core State Standards

CCSS Informational Text 7. Use the illustrations and details in a text to describe its key ideas. (Also **CCSS Informational Text 1.**, **CCSS Writing 2.**, **CCSS Writing 8.**, **CCSS Language 1.**, **CCSS Language 2.**)

Weekly Test 28 Unit 5 Week 4

Name _____

HIGH-FREQUENCY WORDS

Directions
Fill in the circle next to the word that fills the blank.

1 Marta walks _____ the garden.
- ○ like
- ● through
- ○ one

2 They _____ the house.
- ● built
- ○ look
- ○ green

3 Pablo gets up _____ for school.
- ○ away
- ○ little
- ● early

4 Jen will _____ to read.
- ● learn
- ○ together
- ○ laugh

5 Dan likes his _____ class.
- ○ eat
- ● science
- ○ have

GO ON

Common Core State Standards

Questions 1–5: CCSS Foundational Skills 3.g. Recognize and read grade-appropriate irregularly spelled words.

PHONICS

Directions

Fill in the circle next to the answer that shows the correct way to divide the underlined word into syllables.

6 We like to eat <u>oatmeal</u>.

- ○ oatme | al
- ● oat | meal
- ○ oa | tmeal

7 The boy saw a <u>football</u> in the park.

- ● foot | ball
- ○ fo | otball
- ○ footb | all

Directions

Fill in the circle next to the answer.

8 I <u>saw</u> my best friend last night.

Which word has the same sound as <u>aw</u> in <u>saw</u>?

- ● call
- ○ sport
- ○ shore

9 <u>Auto</u> is another word for car.

Which word has the same sound as <u>au</u> in <u>auto</u>?

- ○ phone
- ○ hole
- ● yawn

10 I have a striped cat with four white <u>paws</u>.

Which word has the same sound as <u>aw</u> in <u>paws</u>?

- ○ crown
- ● cause
- ○ roll

GO ON

Common Core State Standards

Questions 6–7: CCSS Foundational Skills 3.e. Decode two-syllable words following basic patterns by breaking the words into syllables.
Questions 8–10: CCSS Foundational Skills 3. Know and apply grade-level phonics and word analysis skills in decoding words.

COMPREHENSION

How to Grow Flowers for Your Mother

First, set aside some space in the garden. Make sure the flowers will get lots of sun.

Put the seeds in the soil. Then cover the seeds with a little more soil.

After that, water the seeds. Water them every two days. If it rains, you can skip that day.

Then watch the flowers grow! Pull up any weeds and throw them away.

When the flowers are all grown, pick some! Take them into the house. Put them in a vase of water. Give them to your mother for a surprise!

GO ON

Directions
Fill in the circle next to the answer.

11 What is the first thing you need to do?

- ○ Give your mother the flowers.
- ○ Scatter the flower seeds.
- ● Set some space aside in the garden.

12 What do you do after you pick the flowers?

- ● Take them inside and put them in a vase.
- ○ Water them once every two days.
- ○ Pull any weeds and throw them away.

13 What do you do just before you give your mother the flowers?

- ○ Watch the flowers grow.
- ○ Scatter the flower seeds.
- ● Put the flowers in a vase.

14 What do you do while you watch the flowers grow?

- ○ Cover the seeds with soil.
- ● Pull up weeds and throw them away.
- ○ Take the flowers into the house.

15 What is the very last step?

- ○ Watch the flowers grow.
- ○ Let the flowers get lots of sun.
- ● Give the flowers to your mother.

GO ON

⟩ **Common Core State Standards**

Questions 11–15: CCSS Informational Text 3. Describe the connection between two individuals, events, ideas, or pieces of information in a text.

Name _____

WRITTEN RESPONSE TO THE SELECTION

Look Back and Write Look back at pages 177–181. What
was Aleck Bell like when he was a boy? Write about it.

Use the list in the box below to help you as you write.

REMEMBER—YOU SHOULD

  tell what Aleck Bell was like as a boy.

☐ use details from the story to describe Aleck's childhood.

☐ try to use correct spelling, capitalization, punctuation, grammar,
and sentences.

Common Core State Standards

CCSS Writing 2. Write informative/explanatory texts in which they name a topic, supply some facts about the topic, and provide some
sense of closure. (Also **CCSS Infomational Text 1., CCSS Language 1., CCSS Language 2.**)

Name _____

HIGH-FREQUENCY WORDS

Directions
Fill in the circle next to the word that fills the blank.

1 Jennifer _____ the telephone.
- ○ please
- ● answered
- ○ snake

2 My sister and I look very _____.
- ○ under
- ○ red
- ● different

3 I can _____ the heavy books.
- ○ sit
- ○ stacked
- ● carry

4 The painter did a _____ job on the porch.
- ○ white
- ● poor
- ○ start

5 He never _____ my question.
- ● answered
- ○ mind
- ○ lived

GO ON

1 Copyright © Pearson Education, Inc., or its affiliates. All Rights Reserved.

Common Core State Standards

Questions 1–5: CCSS Foundational Skills 3.g. Recognize and read grade-appropriate irregularly spelled words.

PHONICS

Directions
Fill in the circle next to the word that fills the blank.

6 When you _____ your story, try to make it better.

- ○ unwrite
- ● rewrite
- ○ prewrite

7 I am _____ of which way to go.

- ○ insure
- ○ resure
- ● unsure

8 Let's _____ the broken model from the start.

- ● rebuild
- ○ unbuild
- ○ semibuild

Directions
Fill in the circle next to the answer.

9 Most of the cake is gone.

Which word has the same sound as <u>o</u> in <u>most</u>?

- ● cold
- ○ mop
- ○ boot

10 The zoo is full of <u>wild</u> animals.

Which word has the same sound as <u>i</u> in <u>wild</u>?

- ○ bin
- ○ mill
- ● find

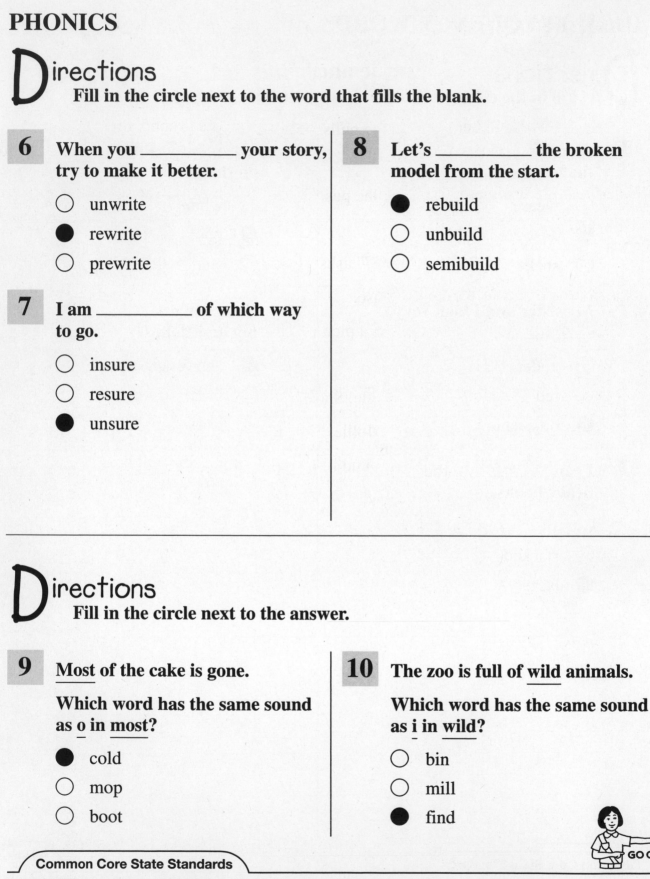

GO ON

Common Core State Standards

Questions 6–10: **CCSS Foundational Skills 3.** Know and apply grade-level phonics and word analysis skills in decoding words.

Name _____

COMPREHENSION

Maggie and Mollie

Maggie works in her garden. She pulls carrots from the ground. She puts them in her basket.

Maggie sees something shiny. She pushes the carrots away. She sees a necklace.

"How did this necklace get here?" asks Maggie. She picks up necklace. She takes the necklace into the house.

Mollie is in the kitchen painting a picture. Her hands are covered in many colors of paint.

"Look what I found," says Maggie. She shows Mollie the necklace.

"That belongs to Millie," says Mollie. "She lost it last week!"

"Let's call her and tell her we found it," says Maggie. "She will be so happy!"

GO ON

Directions
Fill in the circle next to the best answer.

11 This story is mostly about

- ● finding a lost necklace.
- ○ pulling carrots from the ground.
- ○ painting a picture.

12 You can tell that Maggie is

- ○ glad to have a new necklace.
- ○ sad because she lost her necklace.
- ● happy to give the necklace to Millie.

13 Based on the story, how did Millie feel when she lost her necklace?

- ● sad
- ○ happy
- ○ tired

14 You can tell that Mollie and Millie are

- ○ painters.
- ● friends.
- ○ gardeners.

15 Maggie wants to call Millie because

- ● Maggie is a nice person.
- ○ Maggie is a gardener.
- ○ Maggie is a painter.

GO ON

| Common Core State Standards |

Questions 11–15: CCSS Literature 3. Describe characters, settings, and major events in a story, using key details.

Name _____

WRITTEN RESPONSE TO THE SELECTION

Look Back and Write Look back at pages 224–226. What grew in Momoko's stone garden? Write about it. Use evidence from the story to support your answer.

Use the list in the box below to help you as you write.

REMEMBER—YOU SHOULD

☐ tell what grew in Momoko's stone garden.

☐ use words that help readers make a picture in their minds.

☐ try to use correct spelling, capitalization, punctuation, grammar, and sentences.

Common Core State Standards

CCSS Writing 2. Write informative/explanatory texts in which they name a topic, supply some facts about the topic, and provide some sense of closure. (Also **CCSS Literature 1., CCSS Literature 2., CCSS Literature 3., CCSS Language 1., CCSS Language 2.**)